Songs of Dublin

Re-dedicated to the memory of
Joe Holmes, Eddie Butcher and Geordie Hanna,
great singers, now gone.

Songs of
DUBLIN

edited by
Frank Harte

Ossian

First published in 1978 by Gilbert Dalton, Dublin
New edition © 1993 by Ossian Publications, Cork
Copyright © 1993 Frank Harte
Continuity and guitar chords by John Loesberg
Music transcriptions by Manus O'Boyle and John Loesberg
Type-and Music set at Ossian Publications
Cover engraving: *The Carlisle Bridge* (Dublin Penny Journal 1835)
Drawing on p.85 by Brian Lalor

ISBN 0 946005 51 6
OMB 74

The editor and publishers gratefully acknowledge permission to reproduce copyright
material by Paddy Ban O Broin, Patrick Galvin, James Montgomery, Heno Magee, George
Hodnett, Dominic Behan and Brendan Behan.
The Liffeyside and Whack fol the Diddle are published by permission of Waltons, Dublin.
Dublin in my Tears © 1985 by Brendan Phelan.
The Rare oul' Times and When Margaret was Eleven © by Pete St John.
The poem 'Kilmainham Goal, Easter 1991' by permission of Theo Dorgan

Dominic Behan attributes the songs, on which he holds the rights, as follows:
Arkle, words and music by Dominic Behan, © Coda Music, Dicey Reilly, Finnegan's Wake
and The Ragman's Ball, collected from Mary Fitzsimons of Cabra in 1947 and extensively
re-written. New words and music by Dominic Behan. The Twangman and Ye Men of Sweet
Liberties Hall, based on the work of Michael J.Moran (Zozimus). Get me down my Petticoat
collected in childhood from Sergeant-Major R.House of Russell Street and re-written by
Dominic Behan. Building up and Tearing England Down, by Dominic Behan.

OSSIAN PUBLICATIONS LTD.
P.O. Box 84, Cork, Ireland

Contents

INTRODUCTION

And the banshee cried when Dalton died
In the Valley of Knockanure

This is a far cry from Dublin street songs, but it was the first song I heard, sung by a travelling man, that made me aware that we had a tradition of songs telling about the joys and sorrows, the tragedies and battles of a people in a way that I found irresistible. From that first hearing I have been fascinated by the idea of the story told in song.

The stories are told all over the country both in the Irish language and in English, each area adding its own flavour and each singer having his or her own individual style. It would be a brave man who would state 'definitely' that 'this is the correct version' of a song or that 'this is the way' that it should be sung. Who will dare tell Geordie Hanna that his style of singing is wrong, or Eddie Butcher that his version of a song is not correct? Of course his style of singing is right, because that is the way he sings, and of course his version is correct because that is the way he heard it. Whether the air or the verse is different from some other version is of no importance to the singer— he is singing his or her song.

I have been gathering songs around the country for a good number of years now, and seldom have I come across singers who are unwilling to part with their songs. Probably they realise as I do, that the songs do not belong to them, just as they did not belong to the people they got them from. The only reason they have them is to sing them so that others may hear their story. What would we have lost if Brigid Tunney or Sarah Makem or Robert Cinnamond or Elizabeth Cronin, to mention but a few, had refused to sing for fear of another singer getting their song, or if the B.B.C. had kept their now invaluable recordings, collected by Seamus Ennis and Sean O Boyle, locked up for only the ears of the select few ?

The thought of a song dying with its singer or lying in a book or a tape on a shelf gathering dust fills me with horror. If a song is lost, it means the loss of a story that will never again be told, a story told possibly hundreds of years ago that I could have heard again today. A story that could give me an insight into the feelings of the people of that particular time as no history book can. To me songs do not exist on shelves, they exist only in their singing and as such they should be sung and sung again so that the tradition can, if it wishes, carry them on for several hundred years more. While people discuss at length about the folksong revival both in England and America at the present time, and the ethnomusicologists wax eloquent on its various aspects, we in this country have been spared the sacredness of a revival due to the fact that the tradition of singing songs has never died, and with the number of songs and singers around today it is unlikely that it will for some time to come.

Within this tradition of thousands of songs there are songs that can be called Dublin Songs. They have that twist of humour and sarcasm peculiar to the city. Probably the first Dublin songs that I heard were in my father's public house in Chapelizod. Unlike today when one can get a song, complete with air, at one hearing with a tape recorder, the songs at that time came a verse at the time, so that it might take a year or two to get the complete song, depending on how often you met the singer. The Dublin song came into prominence in recent times due in large measure to the complete Dubliner himself— Brendan Behan. Brendan typified all that was Dublin, in his attitudes, his wit, his sarcasm, his songs and the Irish language spoken with a Dublin accent. The impact of The Old Triangle, from his play The Quare Fella, made the public aware that there were Dublin songs other than Molly Malone and The Spanish Lady which, at the time, were sung mainly by the Radio Eireann Singers and the girls with the harps, in much the same manner as Danny Boy is sung. Dominic Behan, the brother, sang a lot more of the songs than Brendan and continued to sing them along with the songs and rhymes he learned from the children playing in the street. Dominic has written many songs himself out of the traditional background, some of which may yet be absorbed into the tradition. Colm O Lochlainn also did much to make the songs known by including in his two fine books of ballads many of the Dublin Street Songs.

Most of the songs included in this selection are well known. I have put them together in answer to the number of people who over the years have asked me for the words of one or other of the songs. The usual request is: 'I have the first verse and the chorus, would you ever give us the rest of it?' I hope this book will fill in the missing verses of quite a few. The notes I have written on the songs come from a very limited knowledge of their background. My hope is that the book will not rest on a shelf but that the songs will be taken and sung and sung again by singers, with or without a voice, and thanks I give to the singers who sang them for me.

Frank Harte
1978

INTRODUCTION TO THE SECOND EDITION

It is fifteen years since this first small collection of Dublin street songs was published by 'Gilbert Dalton' in Dublin, however this edition as you can see is being published by Ossian Publications from Cork, I don't know whether there is anything significant in the shift from Dublin to Cork.

The situation regarding the music continues to grow stronger every day, the younger musicians are excelling their elders in virtuosity while in combination with the fantastic revival of set dancing there are more venues for playing than ever before. It is a pity that one hears the slow air played so seldom in the session today, it was always considered an essential part of a musician's repertoire and no session would finish without one or two being played. Those who are teaching today might do more to encourage the younger students to learn and play the slow airs.

The venues for singing the unaccompanied song however are on the decline. Sessions such as the great 'Tradition Club' in Slattery's of Capel Street or the Sunday morning session with Mary Cooney in the Brazen Head are no more. The Goleen Club over 'The Ferryman' pub on Friday night provides at the present time probably the best opportunity for hearing the unaccompanied song in Dublin.

The intervening years have taken a great toll of the stalwarts of the tradition, musicians and singers . . .Eddie Butcher, Joe Holmes, Geordie Hanna, Breandan Breathnach, Dan O'Dowd, Matt Kiernan, John Egan, Seosamh O hEanai, Seamus Ennis, Luke Kelly, Tom Lenihan, Mikey Flanagan, Nora Cleary, Darach O Cathain, Maire Aine Ni Donnchada, Dominic Behan and Ewan McColl. Looking at what is a very incomplete list of important people lost to the tradition I find it hard to imagine where their replacements are going to come from.

I would like to pay a special tribute to the last two people mentioned, Dominic Behan and Ewan McColl, for between them they made us aware of the harsh song of the street, the unsentimental urban song contrasted with the rural love song. Not only did they both issue collections of songs in print but they left us with a fine legacy of recordings demonstrating their own individual styles of singing. There is a record issued by Topic Records called "Streets of Song" where they contrast the children's songs of Ireland and Scotland showing a great similarity of expression. They were both well aware of the hardship endured by the Irish navvy on the building sites of England in the fifties and have left us a valuable record of that particular time in song and their radio documentary. The popularity and recognition of the Dublin song is due in great measure to the singing of Dominic Behan down through the years, for a long time he was ploughing a lone furrow.

While I lament the loss of singing venues, one cannot but be amazed at the amount of new songs that are coming out almost daily. There are songs being written on almost every subject imaginable, from the troubles in Belfast and Derry to the Moving Statues of Ballinspittle, to the proliferation of fast food outlets, the release of the "Guildford Four' or how Brian O'Lynn took a leaf out of Ned Kelly's book and became a bank robber. Pete St.John has written songs from Dublin's past that I feel have a good chance of being adopted by the tradition and carried along with the Biddy Mulligans and the Dicey Rileys for some time to come.

Again, as before, I would ask the institutions that have so many great songs on tape which were collected from singers all over the country, many of whom are long since dead, to make them available on cassettes to the younger singers so that they might live again through their singing. Brendan Kenneally has written a poem called 'Living Ghosts' in which he says :

'All songs are living ghosts and long for a living voice'

I am afraid that there are still too many 'Living Ghosts' just lying on shelves gathering dust, it is time that they got an airing.

As always my thanks I give to the singers who sang the songs for me

Frank Harte
Chapelizod, 1993

BIDDY MULLIGAN

I'm a buxom fine widow, I live in a spot, In Dub- lin they call it the Coombe. My shop and my stall is laid out on the street And my pal-ace con-sists of one room. At Patrick Street cor-ner for forty-five years I stood there I'm telling no lie And while I stood there sure no body would dare To say black was the white of my eye.

Chorus:

You may travel from Clare to the County Kil- dare, From Drogheda right back by Macroom, But where would you see a fine widow like me, Biddy Mulligan the pride of the Coombe, my boys, Biddy Mulligan the pride of the Coombe.

I sell apples and oranges, nuts and split peas,
Bananas and sugar stick sweet;
Of a Saturday night I sell second-hand clothes
And the floor of my stall is the street.
I sell fish of a Friday laid out on a dish,
Fresh mackerel and lovely ray.
I sell lovely herrings, such lovely fresh herrings,
That once swam in dear Dublin Bay.

Chorus

Now I have a son, Mick, and he plays on the flute,
He belongs to the Longford Street band,
And it would do your heart good for to see him march out
When the band goes to Dollymount Strand.
In the Park of a Sunday I cut quite a dash
All the neighbours look on in surprise
At my grand paisley shawl and my bonnet so tall
Would dazzle the sight of your eyes.

Chorus

A song of fairly recent origin and made famous by the late Jimmy O'Dea. Jimmy, who had all the humour of Dublin, adopted the character of Biddy Mulligan, the street stall-holder, and made her famous in his various pantomime roles.

The street stalls have long since gone from Patrick Street but still can be seen in Thomas Street and Moore Street and, although threatened with deportation from Moore Street, hopefully they will survive for another while yet.

MOLLY MALONE

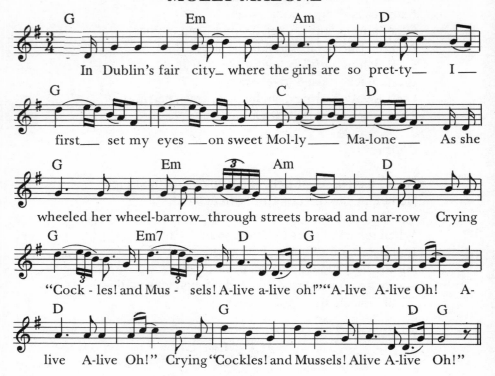

In Dublin's fair city_ where the girls are so pret-ty_ I_ first_ set my eyes _on sweet Mol-ly_ Ma-lone_ As she wheeled her wheel-barrow_ through streets broad and nar-row Crying "Cock-les! and Mus-sels! A-live a-live oh!""A-live A-live Oh! A-live A-live Oh!" Crying "Cockles! and Mussels! Alive A-live Oh!"

She was a fish-monger and sure 'twas no wonder
For her father and mother were fishmongers too,
And each wheeled their barrow through the streets broad and narrow,
Crying "Cockles! and Mussels! Alive! Alive-Oh!"

She died of the fever and no one could save her
And that was the end of sweet Molly Malone
But her ghost wheels her barrow through streets broad and narrow
Crying "Cockles and Mussels ! Alive Alive-Oh!"

I know nothing of the origins of this song and I have not met anybody else who knows any more than myself. I was asked by an American, who was doing research into the shell-fish industry in Ireland, if I could tell him anything about the song, as he was sure that Molly had died from typhoid fever which she picked up from eating the mussels. I had to tell him that he already knew more than I did about the song. Unfortunately this is one of the songs that one hears sung more often by the refined singers than by the ballad singer.

DOWN BY THE LIFFEYSIDE

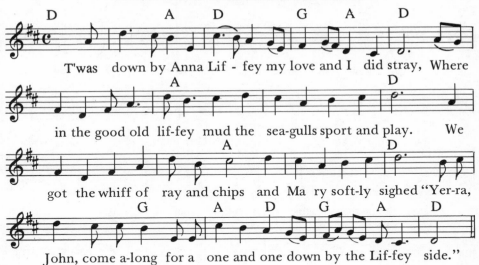

T'was down by Anna Lif-fey my love and I did stray, Where in the good old lif-fey mud the sea-gulls sport and play. We got the whiff of ray and chips and Ma ry soft-ly sighed "Yer-ra, John, come a-long for a one and one down by the Lif-fey side."

And up to Rabiotti's together we did go
And the rapture there that filled our hearts no poet e'er could know.
We started eating one and ones and Mary softly sighed,
"Oh! I'd live forever eating chips down by the Liffey side."

Then out along by George's Street the loving pairs to view,
While Mary swanked it like a queen in a suit of royal blue.
Her coat was newly turned and her blouse was newly dyed
And you couldn't match her amber locks down by the Liffey side

And it's on her oul melodeon so sweetly she did play
"Goodbye and Don't Sigh" and "Rule Britann-i-ay."
But when she turned Sinn Féiner sure me heart near burst with pride
For to hear her sing the Soldier's Song down by the Liffey side.

And on Sunday morning early to Meath Street we will go
And it's up to Father Murphy we both will make our vow,
He'll join our hands in wedlock bands and soon we'll be outside
For the whole afternoon on our honeymoon down by the Liffey side.

This song was written by Peadar Kearney and has always been popular in Dublin. It is one of those songs of which most people have a verse or two, but not the whole song. Peadar Kearney wrote numerous ballads, mainly of a political nature with a Dublin setting. He also wrote the National Anthem, "The Soldier's Song," which is referred to in this song.

RAGLAN ROAD

On Raglan Road of an Autumn day, I saw her first and knew, That her dark hair would weave a snare that I might one day rue I saw the danger yet I passed, along the enchanted way, And I said let grief be a fallen leaf at the dawning of the day.

On Grafton Street in November we tripped lightly along the ledge
Of a deep ravine where can be seen the worth of passion play.
The Queen of hearts still making tarts, and I not making hay.
Oh, I loved too much and by such and such
Is happiness thrown away.

I gave her gifts of the mind, I gave her the secret signs
That's known to the artists who have known the true gods of sound and stone
And word and tint I did not stint, but I gave her poems to say.
With her own name there and her own dark hair.
Like clouds over fields of May.

On a quiet street where old ghosts meet, I see her walking now
Away from me so hurriedly, my reason must allow.
That I have loved not as I should, a creature made of clay.
When the angel woos the clay, he'll lose
His wings at the dawn of the day.

 This is another of those songs that seems to be making its way into the tradition in spite of the fact that it was written by one of our greatest poets, Patrick Kavanagh. Its popularity is due in no small measure to the fact that it was one of the favourite songs of the great Dublin singer Luke Kelly, indeed every time I hear the song the picture of Luke comes to mind and the force with which he used to sing the song. Kavanagh loved the company of women . . .'Surely my God is feminine' . . . as he says they 'fed him praise',

> 'While men the poet's tragic light resented,
> The spirit that is woman caressed his soul.'

Kavanagh's interest in the women of Dublin is easily seen in his poetry,
he remarks on them all, both young and old;

> 'The University girls are like tulip bulbs behind
> More luxurious than ever from Holland was consigned,
> Those bulbs will shortly break in flower
> -rayon silk and cotton
> And our verbal constipation will be totally forgotten.

But Kavanagh loved and lost the woman that he saw in Raglan road that autumn day;

> 'O cruel are the women of Dublin;'s fair city
> They smile and are gone in a flash, . . .
> I knew one in Baggot Street, a medical student
> Unless I am greatly mistaken is she;
> Her smile plays a tune on my trembling psyche
> At thirty yards range, but she passes by me
> In a frost that would make Casanova be prudent.'

The air for the song is taken from an old ballad 'The Dawning of the Day.'

15

THE CRUISE OF THE CALABAR

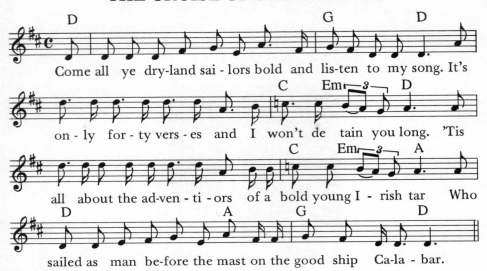

Come all ye dry-land sai-lors bold and lis-ten to my song. It's
on-ly for-ty vers-es and I won't de tain you long. 'Tis
all about the ad-ven-ti-ors of a bold young I-rish tar Who
sailed as man be-fore the mast on the good ship Ca-la-bar.

The captain was a strappin' youth and his height was four-foot-two.
His nose was red and his eyes was black and his hair was a Prussian blue.
He wore a leather medal that he won in the Crimee war,
And his wife was passenger, mate and cook on the good ship Calabar.

We sailed away with a favouring breeze, the weather was sublime.
But just in the straits of Rialto Bridge where you can't pass two at a time
Another craft ran into us, which gave us a serious check.
It stove in the starboard paddle-wheel box and destroyed the hurricane deck.

When huggin' the shore of Inchicore, a very dangerous part,
We ran aground on a lump of coal that wasn't marked on the chart.
And to save ourselves from sinking and to save each precious life
We threw the main deck overboard along with the captain's wife.

Then all became confus-i-on while the stormy winds did blow.
The bosun slipped on an orange peel and fell into the hold below.
The captain cried "'Tis a pirate's rig and on us she does gain.
And the next time I sail for Clondalkin, boys, I'll bloody sure go by train."

We got our ammunition out for to meet the coming foe;
Our cutlasses and boarding pikes and gatlin guns also.
"Put on full steam," the captain cried,"For we are sorely pressed,"
But the engineer from the bank replied,"The oul' horse is doing his best."

Thick and fast the heroes fell, in torrents the blood was spilt.
Great numbers were falling before they were hit to make sure that they
    wouldn't be kilt.
And at last when the pirate surrendered her flag, the crew being all on their
backs,
We found that she was a sister ship with a cargo of cobbler's wax.

Now the ship is in the marine stores now and the crew in the county jail.
And I'm the only survivor left to tell of the terrible tale.
But if I could release that ship I'd sail her off afar,
And an Admiral be of the bloomin' fleet on the fighting Calabar.

I have never yet heard a serious canal song. All of the songs of the canals are satirical. They take the talk and mannerisms of the great sailors, who sailed before the mast, rounded the cape and weathered the storms and transferred them to their sailing on the Royal or Grand Canal. They spoke of "Heaving to in the Bay of Dolphin's Barn," running into hurricanes around Kinnegad and sighting the lighthouse near the Bog of Allen. Even the superstitions of the sea sailors were transferred to the dreaded Thirteenth Lock:

"Oh skipper stay," quoth a mariner grey,
Who stood nigh Marrowbone Lane,
"I'm a sailor old and I trow as bold
As roves on this angry main.
Thirteen is still a number ill,
Beware, young man, don't mock".
Right scornfully laughed the captain."See,
I'm bound for the thirteenth lock."

In fact I have it from a canalman that the greatest danger on a barge was fleas. Once they got into a boat it was the devil's own job to get rid of them.

DICEY REILLY

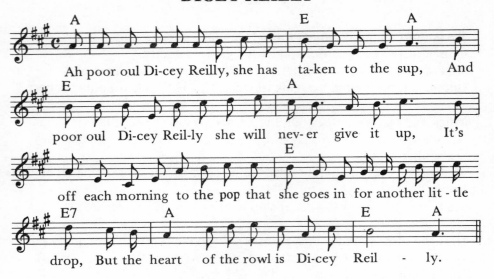

Ah poor oul Di-cey Reilly, she has ta-ken to the sup, And poor oul Di-cey Reil-ly she will nev-er give it up, It's off each morning to the pop that she goes in for another lit-tle drop, But the heart of the rowl is Di-cey Reil - ly.

She will walk along Fitzgibbon Street with an independent air.
And then it's down by Summerhill, and as the people stare
She'll say "It's nearly half-past one, time I went in for another little one."
But the heart of the rowl is Dicey Reilly.

At two, pubs close and out she goes as happy as a lark.
She'll find a bench to sleep it off down in St.Patrick's Park.
She'll wake at five feeling in the pink and say "'Tis time for another drink."
But the heart of the rowl is Dicey Reilly.

She'll travel far to a dock-side bar to have another round,
And after one or two or three she doesn't feel quite sound.
And after four she's a bit unstable, after five underneath the table.
The heart of the rowl is Dicey Reilly.

They carry her home at twelve o'clock, as they do every night.
Bring her inside, put her on the bed and then turn out the light.
Next morning she'll get out of bed and look for a curer for her head.
But the heart of the rowl is Dicey Reilly.

Ah poor oul Dicey Reilly she has taken to the sup.
And poor oul Dicey Reilly she will never give it up.
It's off each morning to the pop, then she goes in for another little drop.
But the heart of the rowl is Dicey Reillly.

Dicey Reilly is a song that has been around for a good while, but again I know nothing of its origin. For years I had only got two verses of the song plus the chorus, then one night at a session I was given the last three verses. Years later when I started singing the complete song, Tom Munnelly said that it was he that had given me the last three verses that he had written to the song.

ARKLE

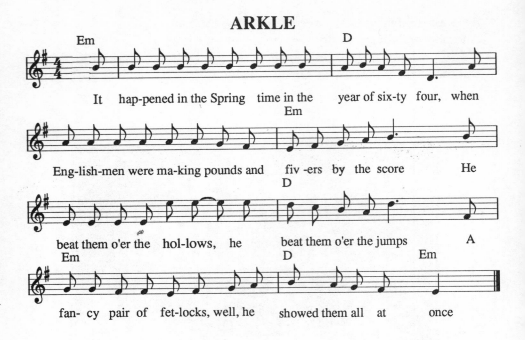

It hap-pened in the Spring time in the year of six-ty four, when
Eng-lish-men were ma-king pounds and fiv-ers by the score He
beat them o'er the hol-lows, he beat them o'er the jumps A
fan- cy pair of fet-locks, well, he showed them all at once

He's English, he's English, as easy might be seen,
With a little bit of Arab stock, but more from Stephen's Green.
Ah, take a look at Millhouse, put out your chest with pride,
He's the greatest steeplechaser on the English countryside.

Then a quiet man called Draper, living in the Emerald Isle,
Says, "This horse of yours called Millhouse, sure he shows a bit of style.
But I've a little fellow and Arkle is his name,
Put your money where you put your mouth and then we'll play the game."

Now the English racing gentlemen, they laughed till fit to burst,
Saying, "You tried before, Tom Draper, and then you came off worst.
If you think your horse can beat us, you're running short in brains,
It's Millhouse that we're speaking of, and not those beastly Danes."

Arkle now is five to two, Millhouse is money-on.
They're off and, dear, I do believe the champion has it won.
There are other horses in the race to test the great chap's might,
But, dearie me, it's plain to see that the rest are out of sight.

There are two more fences now to go, he leads by twenty lengths.
Brave Arkle's putting in a show, poor chap he's all but spent.
Millhouse strides on majestically, great glory in his stride,
The greatest horse undoubtedly within the whole world wide.

Two to go, still Arkle comes, he's cutting down the lead.
But he's beaten bar the shouting for he hasn't got the speed.
From the run up to the last, my God can he hold out,
Look behind you Willie Robinson, and what are you about?

They're at the last and over, Pat Taffe has more in hand.
He's passing England's Millhouse, the finest in the land.
My God, he has us beaten, what can we English say?
The ground was wrong, the distance long, too early in the day.

So come all you gallant Irishmen , wherever you may be,
And let the glasses toast a round to Arkle's victory.
When the English think they've bred a horse to wipe out this disgrace,
Sure we'll send another over for to take great Arkle's place.

This is a recent song written by Dominic Behan to commemorate the great win by Arkle over the
English racehorse, Millhouse, in 1964. Although the song is a recent one, it has exactly the same
feeling as that other song written to celebrate the winning of the Waterloo cup by Master McGrath
almost a century before. The sequence is almost exactly the same as in the earlier ballad, the English
sporting gentlemen laughed at Lord Lurgan when he appeared with his greyhound, and in this song
they laughed at Tom Draper when he appeared with the horse. In each case the revenge was all the
sweeter at the winning post. There are other ballads of this type, whose purpose seems to be to remind
us that we did beat the English, like when Donnelly beat Cooper on the Curragh ofKildare.

DO YOU REMEMBER, JEM ?

I was asked to sing some songs before a play in the Abbey some years ago. The play, by Heno McGee, was called Red Biddy. Heno approached me one night and asked me if I would recite one of his poems. I was very wary at attempting to recite poetry, when Heno assured me that it was a simple Dublin poem called "Do You Remember, Jem?" Well, from that day people have been asking me for the words of it. Heno puts the setting as an old couple in their latter years, sitting on a bench in St.Stephen's Green of a Sunday morning, with the sun shining, and herself gets all romantic about times gone by; while Jem is only waiting for the pubs to open so that he can get a jar, and so she begins. . .

Do you remember, Jem, when we first stepped out,
You'd a pin-striped suit, you wouldn't open your mouth,
But you looked really lovely, 'cept your shirt was stickin' out,
Do you remember, Jem?
Do I remember? Will I ever forget?

And pickin' the winkles on Dollymount strand
And the tide came in, nearly drowned our gran,
We had to push her home in a three-wheeled pram,
Do you remember, Jem?
Do I remember? Will I ever forget?

And the day we went to the Phoenix Park,
To look at the deer and sit on the grass.
And you held my hand and asked for a kiss,
But I wouldn't give in 'cause I knew it was a mortal sin.
Then you said you loved me and promised the ring.
Do you remember, Jem?
Do I remember? Will I ever forget?

And the hooley in the house on Stephen's night.
You met all the relations and nothing went right.
They thought you were my little brother 'cause you looked like Stan,
'Cept he's bigger and he ever got sick over gran.
Do you remember, Jem?
Do I remember? Will I ever forget?

And do you remember the day you changed my name,
You couldn't find the ring and gran started praying.
And she looked in your waistcoat and poked you round.
When she looked through your pockets your trousers fell down.
Do you remember, Jem?
Do I remember? Will I ever forget?

And the singing and dancing back at the house,
Come to think of it you were quiet as a mouse.
You shouldn't have poured whiskey in gran's bottle of stout.
I thought she was dead when we found her asleep in the wedding bed.
But it was gas, and it was grand, and you had to sleep with my brother Stan.
Do you remember, Jem?
Do I remember? Will I ever forget?

Well, it's forty years now we've been knocking about.
You're much the same; I haven't changed,
'Cept my teeth aren't my own and you've got gout.
But you really look lovely, 'cept your shirt's still sticking out.
Do you remember, Jem?
Do I remember? Will I ever forget?

MISS BROWN

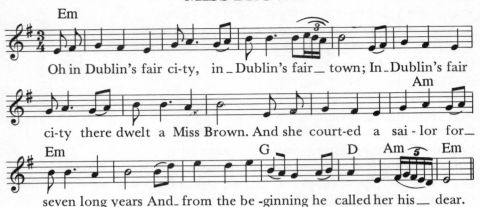

Oh in Dublin's fair ci-ty, in Dublin's fair town; In Dublin's fair
ci-ty there dwelt a Miss Brown. And she court-ed a sai-lor for
seven long years And from the be-ginning he called her his dear.

Then one morning very early all by the break of day,
He came to her cottage and to her did say.
"Rise up, lovely Mary, and come along with me,
Strange things they will happen and strange sights we will see."

Well he took her over mountain and her took her over dell
And they heard through the morning the sound of a bell.
All over the ocean, all over the sea
Ye fair maids of Dublin take warning from me.

"Oh, sailor, oh, sailor, come spare me my life,"
When out of his pocket he drew a sharp knife
And he ripped her and tore her and cut her in three,
And he laid his poor Mary underneath a green tree.

Oh, it's green grows the laurel and red grows the rose
And the raven will follow wherever he goes.
And a cloud will hang over this murderer's head.
He will never rest easy now that Mary be dead.

It's not often that you will hear this song sung in Dublin in spite of its opening lines. In fact when I start to sing this song, people usually expect me to continue with the song on Molly Malone. There are several ballads around the country related to this song, in many cases the ship will not sail, or a storm will rise beacuse there is a murderer on board. The songs make it quite clear that it is very unlucky to go to sea with either a murderer or a pregnant woman.

RED ROSES FOR ME

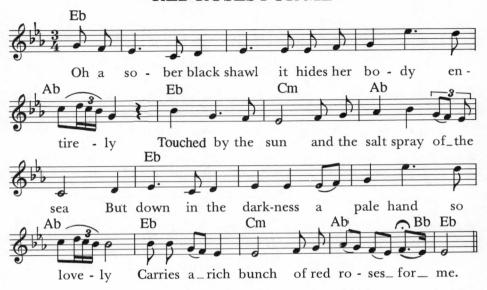

Oh a so-ber black shawl it hides her bo-dy en-tire-ly Touched by the sun and the salt spray of the sea But down in the dark-ness a pale hand so love-ly Carries a rich bunch of red ro-ses for me.

A sober black shawl hides her body entirely,
Touched by the sun and the salt spray of the sea,
But down in the darkness a pale hand so lovely,
Carries a rich bunch of red roses for me.

No arrogant gem is enthroned on her forehead,
Nor hangs from a white ear for all men to see,
But down in the depths of her bosom so pearly,
She carries a rich bunch of red roses for me.

Her petticoat simple, her feet are both bare,
And all that she owns is both neat and scanty,
But there in the deep her eyes are explaining
That she carries a rich bunch of red roses for me.

This beautiful, simple love song was written by the great Dublin dramatist Sean O'Casey for his play of that same name 'Red Roses for Me'. The play was produced in the Olympia in Dublin in 1943. An extract from 'The Essential O'Casey' by Jack Mitchell says 'There are two characters in the play, Eamonn Breydon the son, and Brennan O' The Moor, a retired house painter turned petty landlord who divides his time between singing ballads in the street and worrying whether his money is safe in the vaults of the Bank of Ireland. He and Eamonn make up the music and the words respectively to the song Red Roses for Me.'
Like many of the song that O'Casey wrote for his plays, he set them to well-known airs. This one is sung to the air of 'Eamonn an Chnuic' or' Ned of the Hills'. The title is taken from the old flower symbols, true love being of course symbolised by the red rose.

THE FINDING OF MOSES

On E - gypt's banks, con - ta - gious to the Nile. The
Ould Pharoah's daugh - ter, she went to bathe in style. She
took __ her __ dip and she came un - to the land,
And to dry her royal pelt she ran a - long the strand, A
bull - rush __ tripped her where - up - on she saw __
__ A smil - ing ba - by __ in a wad of straw; She
took __ him __ up and says she in ac - cents mild "Oh
tear - an - a - ges, girls, now, __ which of yis owns the child?"

26

She took him up and she gave a little grin,
For she and Moses were standing in their skin.
"Bedad, now," says she, "It was someone very rude
Left the little baby by the river in his nude."
She took him to her oul lad sitting on the throne
"Da," says she,"Will you give the boy a home?"
"Bedad, now," says he,"Sure I"ve often brought in worse.
Go my darlin daughter and get the child a nurse."

An oul blackamore woman among the crew
Cried out "You royal savage, what's that to do with you?
Your royal ladies is too meek and mild
To beget dishonestly this darling child."
"Ah, then," says Pharoah, "I'll search every nook
From the Phoenix Park down to Donnybrook.
And when I catch hoult of the bastard's father
I will kick him from the Nile down to the Dodder."

Well they sent a bellman to the Market Square,
To see if he could find a slavey there.
but the only one now that he could find
Was the little young one that left the child behind.
She came up to Pharoah, a stranger, *mar dhea*,
Never lettin on that she was the baby's ma.
And so little Moses got his mammy back,
Shows that co-in-ci-dence is a nut to crack.

This song is one of the finest examples of the man they called Zozimus. His name was Michael Moran and he was born in Faddle Alley off the Black Pits in the Liberties of Dublin in 1794, and became blind when he was only two weeks old. Renowned for his extraordinary memory, he became a street-rhymer. The ballads he learned by heart and delivered them with an energy peculiarly his own. His dress is described as a long, coarse, dark, frieze coat with a cape, the lower parts of the skirts being scalloped, an old soft, greasy, brown beaver hat, corduroy trousers and Francis Street brogues, and he carried a long blackthorn stick secured to his wrist with a strap. He took his name from a favourite recitation which he had on Saint Mary of Egypt, who was found by the saintly Abbot Zozimus in the desert. Zozimus died in 1846 at his lodgings in 15 Patrick Street and was buried in Glasnevin cemetery on Palm Sunday. An interesting account of the life and times of Zozimus is given in a little booklet called "Memoir of the Great Zozimus," which finishes with Zozimus' epitaph:

> My burying place is of no concern to me,
> In the O'Connell circle let it be,
> As to my funeral, all pomp is vain,
> Illustrious people does prefer it plain. . .

FINNEGAN'S WAKE

Tim Finnegan lived in Walkin Street, a gentleman Irish mighty odd,

He had a tongue both rich and sweet and to rise in the world he

carried a hod. Now Tim had a sort of a tippling way, With a

love of the liquor poor Tim was born, And to help him on with his

work each day He'd a drop of the cra-tur ev'-ry morn. Whack fol the

da now dance to your partner welt the floor your trotters shake

Was-n't it the truth I told you Lots of fun at Finnegan's Wake.

One morning Tim was rather full.
His head felt heavy which made him shake.
He fell from the ladder and he broke his skull,
So they carried him home, his corpse to wake.
They wrapped him up in a nice clean sheet,
And laid him out upon the bed,
With a gallon of whiskey at his feet
And a gallon of porter at his head.

Chorus

His friends assembled at the wake
And Mrs. Finnegan called for lunch.
First they brought in tay and cakes,
Then pipes, tobaccos and whiskey punch.
Miss Biddy O"Brien began to cry
"Such a neat, clean corpse did you ever see?
Yarrah Tim avourneen, why did you die?"
"Ah, hold your tongue!" says Paddy Magee.

Chorus

Then Biddy O"Connor took up the moan.
"Oh,Biddy," says she,"You're wrong, I'm sure."
But Biddy gave her a belt in the gob
And left her sprawling on the floor.
Oh then the mighty war did rage,
'Twas woman to woman and man to man.
Shillelagh law did all engage
And a row and a ruction soon began.

Chorus

Then Mickey Maloney ducked his head,
When a naggin of whiskey flew at him.
It missed him , falling on the bed.
The liquor splattered over Tim.
Bedad he revives and see how he rises!
And Timothy rising from the bed!
Says "Fling your whiskey round like blazes,
T'anam 'an diabhail, do you think I'm dead?"

Chorus.

A song which has come down in the Dublin tradition, similar in make-up to the Ragman's Ball. I don't know how much influence the ballad had on James Joyce, but he called his great book after this particular song, Finnegan's Wake.

HENRY, MY SON

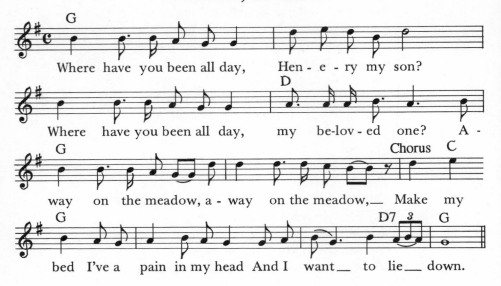

Where have you been all day, Hen - e - ry my son?
Where have you been all day, my be-lov - ed one? A -
way on the meadow, a - way on the meadow,— Make my
bed I've a pain in my head And I want— to lie— down.

And what did you have to eat, Henry, my son?
What did you have to eat, my beloved one?
Poison beans, poison beans.

Chorus

And what will you leave your mother, Henry, my son?
What will you leave your mother, my beloved one?
A wooling vest, a wooling vest.

Chorus

And what will you leave your brother, Henry, my son?
What will you leave your brother, my beloved one?
A blue suit, a blue suit.

Chorus

And what will you leave your father, Henry, my son?
What will you leave your father, my beloved one?
A watch and chain, a watch and chain.

Chorus

And what will you leave your children, Henry, my son?
What will you leave your children, my beloved one?
The sun and moon, the sun and moon.

Chorus

And what will you leave your sweetheart, Henry, my son?
What will you leave your sweetheart, my beloved one?
A rope to hang her, a rope to hang her.

Chorus.

   This song originates from a big classical ballad called Lord Randal. It is probably the only European
ballad which became so strongly traditional in Ireland as to be translated into the Irish language and is
still sung as An Tiarna Randall. The Dublin man could not accept the beautiful, sad, slow, classical
version, but produced instead this inelegant version which is unique, as being the only variant in which
poisoned beans and not eels and eels broth kill the unfortunate youth. The basic story is otherwise
unchanged after nearly four hundred years.

DUBLIN CITY 1913

In Du-blin Ci-ty in nine-teen thir-teen, the boss was rich and he em-ploy'd the slave, The wom-en work'd and the child-ren starved, Till Lar-kin came like a might-y wave. The work-ers cring'd when the boss man thund-ered, And se-ven-ty hours was his week-ly chore, He asked for lit-tle and less was grant-ed., Lest get-ting lit-tle he might ask for more

Then on came Larkin in nineteen thirteen,
A mighty man with a mighty tongue,
The voice of labour, the voice of justice,
And he was gifted and he was young.
God sent us Larkin in nineteen thirteen,
A labouring man with a Union tongue,
He raised the worker and gave him courage,
He was the hero, the worker's son.

It was in August the boss man told us,
That no Union man then for him could work,
We stood by Larkin and told the boss man,
We'd fight or die but we would not shirk.
Eight months we fought and eight months we starved,
We stood by Larkin through thick and thin,
But foodless homes and the crying of children,
They broke our hearts and we could not win.

Then Larkin left us, we seemed defeated,
The night was dark for the working man,
But on came Connolly with new hope and counsel,
His motto was that 'we'd rise again',
In nineteen sixteen in Dublin City,
The English soldiers they burned our town,
They shelled the buildings and shot our leaders,
The harp was buried beneath the crown.

They shot McDermott and Pearse and Plunkett,
They shot McDonagh and Clarke the brave,
From bleak Kilmainham they took their bodies,
To Arbour Hill to a quicklime grave.
But last of all of the seven leaders,
I'll sing the praise of James Connolly,
The voice of labour, the voice of justice,
Who gave his life that men might be free.

The labour song never seemed to take its place in the tradition to any great extent and seldom if ever does one hear a union song sung at a singing session outside of Dublin. I have included two songs in this small collection which deal with the two great Labour leaders, James Connolly and Jim Larkin. Neither of these songs are contemporary but were composed much later by two poets. James Connolly was written by Patrick Galvin and the song on Jim Larkin was written by Donagh McDonagh.
The song deals with the strike which took place in Dublin in 1913, with Jim Larkin leading the strike against the might of William Martin Murphy who persuaded the Dublin employers to lock out any worker who would not agree to resign his membership of the Irish Transport and General Workers Union or give a pledge that he would not become a member of that union. The strike lasted from August 1913 until February of the following year inflicting terrible hardship on the Dublin working class, it was broken as the songs says;

'But foodless homes and crying children
They broke our hearts and we could not win.'

But out of this struggle came the Citizen Army which was to play an important part in the rising of 1916 being led by James Connolly. When the rising was over, William Martin Murphy's newspaper 'The Independent' was in no mood to forget what had happened in 1913 and was to the fore in calling for the death of the leaders of the rebellion and in particular for the death of James Connollly. Donagh McDonagh's song takes the struggle through from 1913 up to the rebellion of 1916 and mentions the death of his own father in the last verse.

'The great appear great because we are on our knees; let us rise.'
Larkin

'And tyranny tramped them in Dublin's gutter until Larkin came along
and cried the call of freedom and the call of pride and slavery crept to its
knees and 1913 cheered from out the utter degradation of their miseries.
Patrick Kavanagh

GEORGE'S QUAY
(or THE FORGETFUL SAILOR)

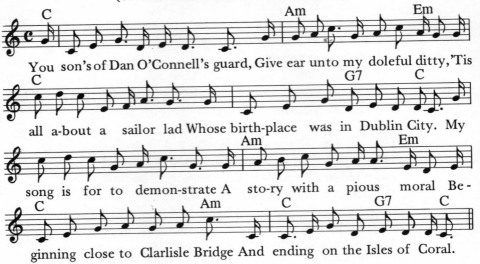

You son's of Dan O'Connell's guard, Give ear unto my doleful ditty, 'Tis all a-bout a sailor lad Whose birth-place was in Dublin City. My song is for to demon-strate A sto-ry with a pious moral Be-ginning close to Clarlisle Bridge And ending on the Isles of Coral.

1

A schooner sailed from George's Quay
  for foreign parts one sultry saison
And on the shore a maiden stood and
  cried like one bereft of raison.
"Och Johnny Doyle me love for you is
  true but full of deep contrition.
For what will all the neighbours say
  about me and me sad condition."

2

The capstan turned and, sails unfurled,
  the schooner scudded down the Liffey.
The damsel gave a piercing shriek, she
  was a mother in a jiffy.
The vessel crossed the harbour bar, her
  course was set for foreign waters,
To China where they're very wise and
  drown at birth their surplus daughters.

3

Now years and years are past and gone
  and Mary's child is self-supporting,
And Mary's heart is fit to break when
  that young buck goes out a-courting.
And so says she on one fine day he'll
  leave me lone and melancholy
I"ll dress me up in sailors' clothes and
  scour the seven seas for Johnny.

4

She shipped aboard a pirate bold, whic
  raided on the hot equator
And with these hairy buccaneers there
  sailed this sweet and verchus crathur.
The Captain thought her name was Bil
  his character was most nefarious,
Consorting with this hainous baste, he
  situation was precarious.

5

'Twas in the Saragossa sea two rakish
  barques were idly rolling
And Mary on the middle watch the
  quarter deck she was patrolling.
She calmly watched the neighbouring ship,
  then suddenly became exclamant,
For there upon the gilded poop stood
  Mr. Doyle in gorgeus raiment.

6

And now they're back in sweet Ringsend
  that gem that sparkles on the Dodder
He lives a peaceful merchant's life and
  does a trade in oats and fodder.
By marriage lines she's Mrs. Doyle, she
  runs a stall of penny winkles
And when he hears "She's that away"
  his single eye with joy it twinkles.

7

Their family now it numbers ten
  and Mary's heart sings like a linnet,
And Johnny's tamed that wild young buck,
  that stretched her patience to the limit.
They are happy there in sweet Ringsend,
  they will sail no more for foreign waters,
For Johnny Doyle his hands are full,
  with fine strong sons and fine sweet daughters.

This song was given to me by the late Colm O'Lochlainn, who published the two very fine books on ballads called "Irish Street Ballads" and "More Irish Street Ballads." He told me he got the song from the author Jimmy Montgomery who was for years the Irish film censor: the wellknown architect and speaker Niall Montgomery was his son.. It tells in fine style the adventures of one Johnny Doyle, who retires eventually, after his adventures on the high seas, to set up an oats and fodder business in sweet Ringsend, the gem that sparkles on the Dodder.

THE LIMB OF THE LAW

You can tell by my feet I'm a limb of the law The people of Dublin for

me have no grá they hiss me and boo me when I pass them by 'Sinn

Féin' 'Up the Rebels' you'll hear them all cry. Now you

may think that's bad but there's one thing that's worse This

grand Ir- ish lang- uage on my soul 'tis a curse with their

yibberin and yabberin like an old ass's bray the

castle expects me to know what they say with 'Och- one' 'Mo bhrón' you'll

hear them all say 'An dtuigeann tú mé' and 'Sinn Féin hooray' 'Is

dóigh liom go bhfuil is is dóigh liom nach é' ach tá mé ag foghlaim an Gaeilge.

I've a friend on the force and he's courting a cook,
And what do you know but she bought him a book
With Irish on this side and English on that.
So small I could carry it round in my hat.
First learn the letters and then the whole phrase,
I"ll have it all off in a couple of days.
Then their yibberin and yabberin I'll soon understand,
Such larnification will stagger the land.

Chorus

This book I procured and to learn I must try
"An bhfuil mé?" means "Are you?", "An bhfuil tú?" means "Am I?"
"Is dóigh liom," I think that I do understand.
"Mo lámh" is my foot and "Mo chluas" is my hand.
"tá mé ag foghlaim," I'm learning you see.
If I keep on like this, an inspector I'll be.
I'm getting so big that I don't know the cat.
My head is two sizes too large for my hat.

Chorus

With larnification I"m bloody near dead
I lie on the floor 'cause I can't lie in bed.
I am walking and talking when I'm fast asleep.
When I hear "Up the rebels!" my flesh starts to creep.
My friends all have left me, I've now just a few.
I'm walking around like a wandering Jew.

Chorus

Around the period of 1916 and afterwards when meetings were being called and speeches were being made in the Irish language against conscription and in favour of national independence, the police were powerless to prosecute the leaders as they could not understand what was being said. Dublin Castle, the police headquarters, then issued instructions for the police to learn Irish so that the speakers could be brought to court and sentenced. The Dublinman, quick to see the humour of the situation, soon put the difficulties of the policeman into song, which was widely sung at that time. I am told that the song was written by Brian O'Higgins.

THE NIGHT BEFORE LARRY WAS STRETCHED

Oh the night be-fore Lar-ry was streched, well the boys they all paid him a vi-sit A bit in their sacks too they fetched, for they sweat-ed their duds till they ris it, For Lar-ry was e-ver the lad when a boy was con-demned to the squee-zer Would fence all the duds that he had for to help a poor friend to a snee-zer

AND WARM HIS GOB BEFORE HE DIED (Spoken)

The boys they came crowding in fast
And they drew all their stools round about him.
Six glims round his trap case was placed
For he couldn't be well waked without them.
When one of them asked could he die
Without having duly repented
Says Larry "That's all in my eye
And first by the clergy invented
FOR TO GET A FAT BIT FOR THEMSELVES."

"Oh I'm sorry, dear Larry," says I,
"For to see you in this situation.
And blister my limbs if I lie
I'd as lief it had been my own station."
"Ochone! It's all over," says he,
"For the neck-cloth I'm forced to put on
And by this time tomorrow you'll see
Your poor Larry as dead as a mutton
BECAUSE WHY, HIS COURAGE WAS GOOD."

"And I'll be cut up like a pie
And my nob from my body be parted."
"You're in the wrong box," then says I,
"For blast me if they're so hard-hearted.
A chalk on the back of your neck
Is all that Jack Ketch dares to give you
Then mind not such trifles a feck
Or why should the likes of them grieve you?
AND NOW BOYS COME TIP US THE DECK."

Well the cards then being called for, they played
Until Larry found one of them cheated
A dart at his napper he made
For the boy, he being easily heated.
"Oh, by the hokey, you thief,
I'll scuttle your nob with me daddle
You cheat me because I'm in grief
But soon I'll demolish your noddle
AND LEAVE YOU YOUR CLARET TO DRINK."

Then the clergy came in with his book
And he spoke so smooth and so civil
Larry tipped him a Kilmainham look
And he pitched his big wig to the devil.
Then, sighing, he threw back his head
For to get a sweet drop of the bottle
And pitiful sighing he said:
"Oh the hemp will soon be round my throttle,
AND CHOKE MY POOR WINDPIPE TO DEATH."

"Oh then sure it's the best way to die
Oh the devil a better a living
For now when the gallows is high
Then your journey is shorter to heaven.
But what harasses Larry the most
And makes his poor soul melancholy
Is he thinks of a time when his ghost
It will come in a sheet to sweet Molly.
OH! SURE 'TWILL KILL HER ALIVE."

So moving, these last words he spoke
We all vented our tears in a shower.
For my own self, I thought my heart broke
For to see him cut down like a flower.
On his travels we watched him next day
The throttler, I thought I could kill him
But Larry not one word did say
Nor change till he come to King William
THEN, MUSHA, HIS COLOUR GREW WHITE.

When he came to the old nubbing chit
He was tucked up so neat and so pretty
The rumbler chugged off from his feet
And he died with his face to the city.
He kicked too but that was all pride
For soon you might see 'twas all over.
Soon after the noose was untied
And at darkey we waked him in clover
AND SENT HIM TO TAKE HIS GROUND SWEAT.

This is only one of a group of execution songs written in Newgate Cant or slang style somewhere around the 1780s, others being The Kilmainham Minuet, Luke Caffrey's Ghost and Larry's Ghost which, as promised in the seventh verse, comes in a sheet to Sweet Molly. The King William, at the sight of which Larry grew pale, was a statue which stood in College Green, but which has since been blown up. Dublin has a terrible history of exploding statues. I first came across this song in a book, the name of which I can't remember, but it attributed the song to a "Hurlfoot Bill Meaghear". The lines spoken between the verses seem to be a standard in this type of song and in some instances read very similar to the writing of James Joyce, like these examples from Luke Caffrey's Ghost:
'He squared up to the two bailies, tipped one of them a loving squeeze then gave him a cut of bread and butter over the elbow and a back sprang in the mazzard that made his daylights dance to the tune of the Old Cow and the Haystack, set him spinning like a whirligig, and laid him down, your soul, amongst the mudlarks, where he slept like a daisy. He then tipped the other a long arm leg, with a dig in the smellers that laid him on his face, when he gave them leg bail for his appearance at the next crack-neck asembly, be the hoky! His eyes were swelled in his brainbox, like two scalded gooseberries in a mutton tart, and his grinders rattled in his jaw-wags, for all the world like a pair of white-headed fortunetellers in an elbow shakers bone-box.'

MY LOVE CAME TO DUBLIN

My love came to Dublin — one fine Sun-day morn-ing, — My— love—came to Dublin— to honour me — there.— He— wore a green rib-bon a-round his blue bon-net —— And I —wore a bangle— of gold — in my hair. ——

The leaves they were green on that fine Sunday morning
But now they are falling, winding about,
And I never asked him to buy me a ring.
Fall down very lightly ye leaves on me now.

The good girls sleep in all their fine modesty
And the bad girls sleep in the height of their shame,
But I must lie lone in the cold by the river
Until I see my true love come back with my name.

I won't ask the clergy for prayers in the chapel
And I won't hear the minister saying the prayers
But I'll go out to the wood of the birch trees and branches
And I'll ask them to raise up their arms in the air.

I will make my love some shoes of the finest Spanish leather
I will make my love a coat of the finest you've ever seen
And he will walk like a lord through the City of Dublin
And I will walk beside him in a mantle of green.

Another song written by Patrick Galvin, a quiet, tender little song which reminds me of that song of Sarah Makem's "The Streets of Derry."

THE RAGMAN'S BALL

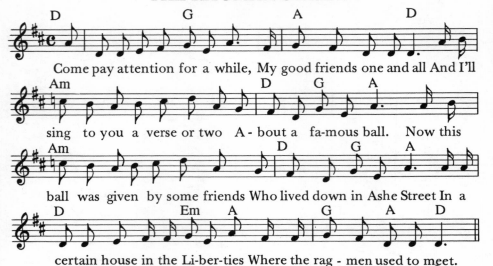

Come pay attention for a while, My good friends one and all And I'll
sing to you a verse or two A - bout a fa-mous ball. Now this
ball was given by some friends Who lived down in Ashe Street In a
certain house in the Li-ber-ties Where the rag - men used to meet.

Well the names were called at seven o'clock
And every man was on the spot
And to show respect to the management
Every ragman brought his mot.
Now I must admit that I brought mine
At twenty-five minutes to eight
And the first to stand up was Kieran Grace
For to tell me that I was late.

Then up jumps Humpy Sudelum
And he says "I think somehow
By the way yis are going on tonight
Yis are looking for a row.
Now look at here Grace if you want your face
You'd better not shout or bawl,
There's a lot of hard chaws to be here tonight
To respect the Ragman's Ball."

Then we all set down some fish and chips
And every man was there
Oh and at the place of honour
Billy Boland took the chair.
Well he swiped the chair and sold it to
An oul one in Carmen Hall
And he danced on the face of Kieran Grace
The night of the Ragman's Ball.

Oh! says my one, "You're a quare one now
And Billy, you're hard to beat,"
When up jumps Liza Boland
And she told her to hold her prate;
But my one made a clout at her
And she missed her and struck the wall
And the two of them went in the ambulance
The night of the Ragman's Ball.

Now to make the thing a swell affair
We brought friends quite a few;
We brought up Blind Gort Whelan
And Big Dan Kenny too.
And the gallant Jack Tar
Smoked his cigar
And he slipped coming through the hall
And he lost a new bag and all his swag
The night of the Ragman's Ball.

Now to keep the house alive, my boys,
We brought musicians too
Oh! we brought up Tommy Reynolds
And his old tin whistle too,
Well he played that night with all his might
Till coming on to dawn
But we couldn't find any to dance with Dan Kenny
The night of the Ragman's Ball.

(continued on page 45)

THE TWANGMAN

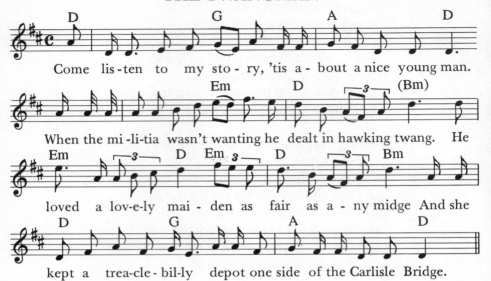

Come lis-ten to my sto-ry, 'tis a-bout a nice young man. When the mi-li-tia wasn't wanting he dealt in hawking twang. He loved a lov-e-ly mai-den as fair as a-ny midge And she kept a trea-cle-bil-ly depot one side of the Carlisle Bridge.

Now another one came courting her
And his name was Micky Bags.
He was a commercial traveller
And he dealt in bones and rags.
Well he took her out to Sandymount
For to see the waters roll
And he stole the heart of the twangman's mot,
Playing Billy in the bowl.

Now when the twangman heard of this
He flew into a terrible rage,
And he swore by the contents of his twang cart
On him he'd have revenge.
So he lay in wait near to James's Gate
And when poor oul Bags came up
With his Twangknife sure he took the life
Of the poor oul gather-em-up.

44

And it's now yis have heard my story
And I hope yis'll be good men
And not go chasing the Twangman's mot
Or any other oul hen.
For she'll leave you without a brass farthing,
Not even your oul sack of rags
And you'll end up in the gutter there
Like poor oul Mickey Bags.

This song is often said to have been written by Zozimus. I don't believe that it was. Surely a song as
good as this would have been included in the memoirs of Zozimus if it had been written by him. It tells
of the terrible revenge of the Twangman. Twang, I am told, was a kind of sweetmeat and Treacle
Billy was a kind of toffee. The Carlisle Bridge referred to is now O'Connell Bridge. I don't know what
the "Billy in the Bowl" he was playing out at Sandymount was, but there was a character called Billy
in the Bowl. He was born without any legs and used to propel himself around the streets in an iron
bowl with his hands. He was eventually convicted of killing a man and ended his life in jail.

(The Ragman's Ball - Continued)

For eating we had plenty there
As much as we could hold.
We drank Brady's loop-line porter
Until round the floor we rolled.
In the midst of the confu-si-on
Someone shouted for a song
When up jumps oul Dunlavin and sings
'Keep rolling your barrel along.'

Then we all sat down to some ham-parings
When everything was quiet
And for broken noses I must say
We had a lovely night.
Black eyes they were in great demand
Not to mention split heads and all.
So if anyone wants to commit suicide
Let them come to the Ragman's Ball.

A song of the same type as Finnegan's Wake which lists off the names and antics of some well-known
characters of the time. The song is dated by the reference to "Brady's Loop-line Porter," which refers
to the time when the Loop-Line railway from Westland Row to Amien's Street Station was being built.
Porter in that area was being sold at 1 1/2 pence a pint, against two pence a pint in the rest of Dublin.
Colm said that Arigho, who printed the ballad, was persecuted for a long time afterwards by the
various notabilities mentioned in it.

THE ROW IN THE TOWN

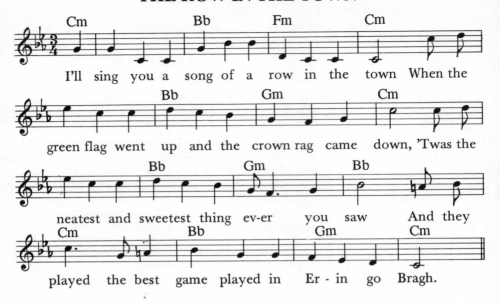

I'll sing you a song of a row in the town When the
green flag went up and the crown rag came down, 'Twas the
neatest and sweetest thing ev-er you saw And they
played the best game played in Er - in go Bragh.

Well a thousand brave men now of every degree
With their rifles and bayonets they swore they'd be free
And one fine Easter morning they laughed at the law
And they played the best game played in Erin go Bragh.

God rest gallant Pearse and his comrades who died
Tom Clarke, McDonagh, McDermott, McBride.
And here's to Jem Connolly who gave one hurrah
As he placed the machine guns for Erin go Bragh.

And brave De Valera was down at Ringsend
The honour of Ireland to hold and defend.
He had no veteran soldiers but volunteers raw
Making sweet Mauser music for Erin go Bragh.

Bold Kent and his comrades like lions at bay
From the South Dublin Union poured death and dismay.
And what was their wrath when those Englshmen saw
All the dead khaki soldiers in Erin go Bragh.

And here's to Ned Daly and all his command
From the Four Courts to Broadstone their fighting was grand.
For the might of the empire they cared not a straw
And they played the best game played in Erin go Bragh.

Now our brave English captain was raving that day
Saying: "Give me one hour and I'll blow them away."
But a big Mauser bullet got stuck in his craw
And he died of lead poisoning, Erin go Bragh.

Here's health to the men of the brave rank and file
And the loyal-hearted women of Erin's Green Isle.
Let true men salute them in wonder and awe
The bravest and greatest in Erin go Bragh.

All honour to Dublin, to her's the renown
In the long generations her name will go down.
And their children will tell how their forefathers saw
The red blaze of freedom o'er Erin go Bragh.

Another song of the 1916 rebellion. The version given here has, I think, most of the verses; but then one can never be sure. Again it has all the satirical humour of the Dubliner, even the title of the song which refers to the rebellion from which the freedom we have came as a little "Row in the town." The song was written by Peadar Kearney.

THE SPANISH LADY

As I went out through Dublin City At the hour of
twelve of the night Who should I see but a Spa-nish la-dy
Washing her feet by can-dle light. First she washed them and
then she dried them, O - ver a fire of am-bry coals. In
all my life I never did see a__ maid so sweet a - bout the soles.

Chorus:
Whack fol the toor a loor a laddy Whack fol the toor a loor a lay.
Whack fol the toor a loor a laddy Whack fol the toor a loor a lay.

I stopped to look but the watchman passed,
Says he: "Young fellow the night is late
Along with you home or I will wrestle you
Straight away through the Bridewell gate."
I threw a look to the Spanish lady
Hot as the fire of ambry coals
In all my life I ne'er did see
Such a maid so neat about the soles.
Chorus

As I walked back through Dublin City
As the dawn of day was o'er
Who should I see but the Spanish lady
When I was weary and footsore.
She had a heart so filled with loving
And her love she longed to share
In all my life I never did meet
With a maid who had so much to spare.
Chorus

Now she's no mot for a puddle swaddy
With her ivory comb and her mantle so fine.
But she'd make a wife for the Provost Marshall
Drunk on brandy and claret wine.
I got a look from the Spanish lady
Hot as a fire of ambry coals.
In all my life I never did meet
With a maid so neat about the soles.
Chorus

I've wandered north and I've wandered south
By Stoney Batter and Patrick's Close
Up and around by the Gloucester Diamond
And back by Napper Tandy's house.
Old age has laid her hand upon me
Cold as a fire of ashy coals
And gone is the lonely Spanish lady
Neat and sweet about the soles?
Chorus

As I was leaving Dublin City
On that morning sad of heart
Lonely was I for the Spanish lady
Now that forever we must part.
But still I always will remember
All the hours we did enjoy
But then she left me sad at parting
Gone forever was my joy.
Chorus

This is another of those songs which I remember from childhood but know absolutely nothing about except that it continues to grow as I hear new verses to it year after year. For too long this song has been sung with quiet accompaniment instead of the unaccompanied voice. There are several versions of the song, some of which seem to have come back from America.

YE MEN OF SWEET LIBERTIES

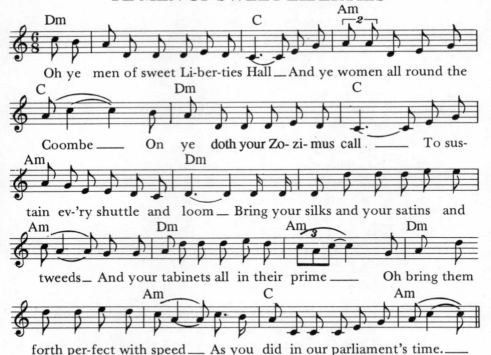

Oh ye men of sweet Li-ber-ties Hall — And ye women all round the Coombe — On ye doth your Zo- zi- mus call . — To sus-tain ev'-ry shuttle and loom — Bring your silks and your satins and tweeds — And your tabinets all in their prime — Oh bring them forth per-fect with speed — As you did in our parliament's time. —

Let us sing of the Coombe and each street
Long before the vile Union was known
When the lords and the nobles did meet
And around us a glory had thrown.
Then high were Newmarket and Court,
The Chambers, The Poddle, The Manor
Where thousands each day did resort
Placing trade on the Liberties banner.

Sing Brown Street and Sweet Warren Mount
Faddle Alley and then the oul Blackpits
Which hear from me their full account
And where I have made my best hits.
There is Cork Street and Mill Street and John Street
With their various alleys and lanes
With Marrowbone Lane ever sweet
Where strong water got ever more reigns.

Sing the streets of Ardee, Meath and Dean,
Thomas, Francis and dear Ashe of old,
With her chapels and schools which retain
A spirit unbroken and bold.
Then up with the fringes once more
And let Erin have justice and joys,
Free trade and home rule restore
And the rights of the Liberty boys.

This song was written by the great Zozimus as a protest against, as he says, 'the vile Act of Union.'

WHACK FOL THE DIDDLE

I'll sing   you a song of peace and love. Whack fol the did-dle

all the di doh day. To the   land   that reigns all   lands a-bove

Whack fol the diddle all the di do day. May peace and plen-ty

be her share Who kept our homes from want and care, God

bless mother England is our prayer.Whack fol the diddle all the di do day.

Whack fol the diddle all the di do day   So we say,   hip hooray,

Come and listen while we pray. Whack fol the diddle all the di do day.

When we were savage, fierce and wild, Whack etc.
She came like a mother to her child, Whack etc.
She gently raised us from the slime
Kept our hands from hellish crime
And sent us to heaven in her own good time, Whack etc.

Chorus

Our fathers oft were very bad boys, Whack etc.
Guns and pikes are dangerous toys, Whack etc.
From Bearna Baol to Bunker Hill
They made poor England weep her fill
But oul Brittannia loves us still, Whack etc.

Chorus

Now, Irishmen forget the past! Whack etc.
And think of the time that's coming fast! Whack etc.
When we shall all be civilised,
Neat and clean and well-advised.
Now won't Mother England be surprised? Whack etc.

Chorus

 Here again Peadar Kearney uses his sarcasm to great effect, it being the strongest weapon available to
the people at the time. "Oh won't Mother England be surprised! Whack fol the diddle..."

THE OUL' TRIANGLE

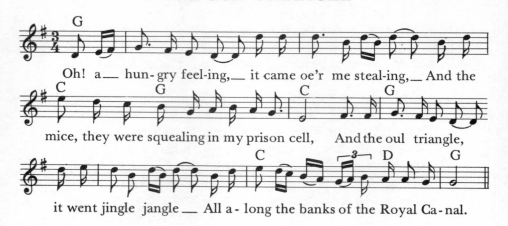

Oh! a hun-gry feel-ing, it came oe'r me steal-ing, And the mice, they were squealing in my prison cell, And the oul triangle, it went jingle jangle — All a-long the banks of the Royal Ca-nal.

To begin the morning, the screw was bawling
'Ah ! get up you bowsey and clean out your cell !'
Chorus

The screw was peeping while the lag was sleeping
And he was dreaming of his gal, Sal
Chorus

In the female prison there are seventy women
And it's among those women I would like to dwell,
Chorus

Now the wind was rising and the sun declining
While I lay there pining in my prison cell.
Chorus

I don't know whether Brendan Behan wrote this song or not but he certainly brought it to the public's attentention by including it in his play which he wrote against capital punishment and hanging in particular, 'The Quare Fella'. It also made people aware that there were Dublin songs other than Molly Malone and The Spanish Lady, sung to harp accompaniment.

YOUNG EMMET

In Green Street courthouse in eight-teen and three Stood young
Em-met the he-ro true and brave — For fighting the ty-rant, his
coun-try to free And to tear from her brow the name of slave.
There are still men in Ire-land both loy-al and true Who remember her patriots with pride And with God's help, young Emmet, —
we'll still give to you The ep-i-taph unwrit-ten since you died.

The verdict was 'Guilty,' the sentence was death
And in Thomas Street the tyrant's work was done
But young Emmett smiled as he drew his last breath
For he knew the fight for freedom would be won.
Chorus
Alone and defiant he stood in the dock
While Lord Norbury, the hanging judge, looked down.
Against his false charges he stood firm as a rock
Yet another Irish martyr to the crown.
Chorus

There is an older song called Bold Robert Emmet the Darling of Erin, but I always found the verses to be so contrived that I was never quite comfortable singing it. After all Robert Emmett was hanged, drawn and quartered and yet Bold Robert Emmett will die with a smile or another verse that begins with 'Hark the bells tolling' never seemed to fit well enough together for my liking. I heard this song only recently from the author, Paddy Bán O Broin, a Wicklow man living in Dublin, probably better known for his flute playing and dancing.

THREE LOVELY LASSIES FROM KIMMAGE

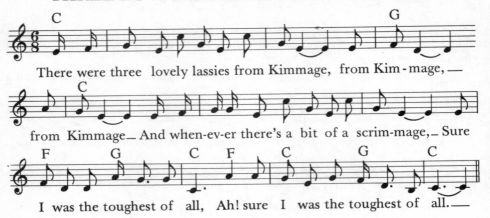

There were three lovely lassies from Kimmage, from Kimmage, from Kimmage
And whenever there's a bit of a scrimmage,
Sure I was the toughest of all, Ah ! sure I was the toughest of all.

Now the cause of the row was Joe Cashin, Joe Cashin, Joe Cashin,
For he told me he thought I looked smashin'
At a dance in the Adelaide Hall, at a dance in the Adelaide Hall.

When he gets a few jars he goes frantic, oh ! frantic, oh ! frantic,
But he's tall and he's dark and romantic
And I love him in spite of it all, and I love him in spite of it all.

Now the other two young ones was flippin', they were flippin', they were flippin'
When they saw me and Joe and we trippin'
To the strains of the Tennessee Waltz, to the strains of the Tennessee Waltz.

Now he told me he thought we should marry, should marry, should marry,
For he said it was foolish to tarry
So I lent him the price of the ring, Oh ! I lent him the price of the ring.

Now my da says he'll give us a present, a present, a present,
An oul' stool and a lovely stuffed pheasant
And a picture to hang on the wall, and a picture to hang on the wall.

I went down to the Tenancy Section, the section, the section,
The T.D., just before the election
Said he'd get me a house near my ma, yes ! he'd get me a house near my ma.

Well we're getting the house, the man said it, now he said it, he said it.
When I've five or six kids to my credit
In the meantime we'll live with my ma, in the meantime we'll live with my ma.

The great Delia Murphy made famous a song called the Three Lovely Lassies from Bannion some years ago, but the Dubliner again, not to be outdone, took the song and twisted it to suit his own location. The song is set in Dublin about twenty-five years ago. I got it from Luke Kelly.

THE DUBLIN JACK OF ALL TRADES

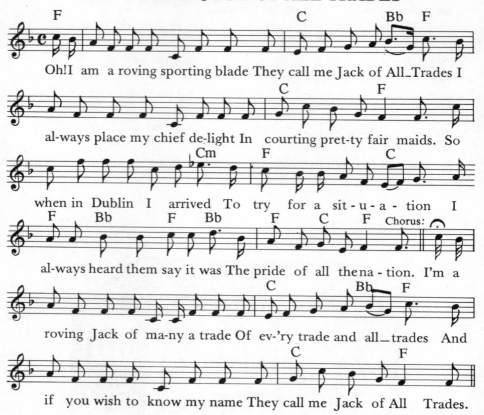

Oh! I am a roving sporting blade They call me Jack of All Trades I
al-ways place my chief de-light In courting pret-ty fair maids. So
when in Dublin I arrived To try for a sit-u-a-tion I
al-ways heard them say it was The pride of all the na-tion. I'm a
roving Jack of ma-ny a trade Of ev-'ry trade and all trades And
if you wish to know my name They call me Jack of All Trades.

O ! on George's Quay I first began
And there became a porter
Me and my master soon fell out
Which cut my acquantaince shorter.
In Sackville Street a pastry cook
In James's Street a baker
In Cook Street I did coffins make
In Eustace Street a preacher.

Chorus

In Baggot Street I drove a cab
And there was well requited
In Francis Street had lodging beds
To entertain all strangers.
For Dublin is of high renown
Or I am much mistaken
In Kevin Street, I do declare,
Sold butter, eggs and bacon.

Chorus

3 In Golden Lane I sold oul shoes
In Meath Street was a grinder
In Barrack Street I lost my wife
And I'm glad I ne'er could find her.
In Mary's Lane I've dyed old clothes
Of which I've often boasted
In that noted place, Exchequer Street
Sold mutton ready roasted.

Chorus

4 In Temple Bar I've dressed old hats
In Thomas Street a sawyer
And in Pill Lane I sold a plate
In Green Street was a lawyer,
In Plunkett Street I sold cast clothes
In Bride's Alley was a broker
In Charles' Street I had a shop
Sold shovel, tongs and poker.

Chorus

5 In College Green a banker was
In Smithfield was a drover
In Britain Street a waiter and
In George's Street a glover.
On Ormond Quay I sold old books
In King Street was a nailer
In Towsend Street a carpenter
And in Ringsend a sailor.

Chorus

6 In Cole's Lane was a butcher
And in Dame Street was a tailor
In Moore Street a chandler
And on the Coombe a weaver.
In Church Street there I sold oul ropes
On Redmond's Hill a draper
In Mary Street sold 'bacco pipes
In Bishop Street a Quaker.

Chorus

7 In Peter Street I was a quack
In Greek Street was a grainer
On the harbour I did carry sacks
In Werbergh Street a glazier.
In Mud Island was a dairy boy
Where I became a scooper
In Capel Street a Barber's Clerk
In Abbey Street a cooper.

Chorus

8 In Liffey Street had furniture
With fleas and bugs I sold it
And at the bank a big placard
I often stood to hold it.
In New Street I sold hay and straw
In Spittlefields made bacon
In Fishamble Street was at the grand
Old trade of basket-making.

Chorus

9 In Summerhill a coach-maker
In Denzil Street a gilder
In Cork Street was a tanner
And in Brunswick Street a builder.
In High Street I sold Hosiery
In Patrick Street sold all blades
So if you wish to know my name
They call me Jack of All Trades.

This is a standard type of ballad that has been written about many towns. It is not peculiar to Dublin alone. It calls out the various streets and then tells of the trades carried out in them. It is interesting to ramble around Dublin and still see the same occupations as listed in the song carried on in the same streets, although you may have to root much harder today to find the small shops.

MONTO

Well if you've got a wing O! Take her up to Ring O! Where the
waxies sing O! All the day. If you've had your fill of por-ter And you
can't go a-ny further Give your man the or-der "Back to the quay!

Chorus:
And take her up to Mon-to, Mon-to, Mon-to,
Take her up to Mon-to, lan-ge-roo, to you!

Did ya hear of Buckshot Forster, the dirty ould imposthor —
Got a mot and lost her in the Furry Glen —
So he just put on his bowler, and he buttoned up his trowser
Then he whistled for a growler, and he said: 'My man' (this in a posh accent)

(*Chorus*) : Take me up to Monto, etc.

You have heard of the Dublin Fusileers, the dirty ould bamboozeleers
They went and killed the childer, 1, 2, 3..
Marchin' from the Linenhall, there's one for every cannonball,
And Vicky's going to send 'em all o'er the sea:

(*Chorus*) : But first go up to Monto, etc.

When Carey told on skin-the-Goat, O'Donnell got him in the boat —
He wished he'd never bin afloat, the dirty skite;
He wasn't very sensible to tell on the Invincibles,
They stuck up for their principles day and night . . . by

(Chorus) : Goin' up to Monto, etc

Oh . . .when the Czar of Rooshia and the King of Prooshia
Landed in the Phaynix in a big ball-oo-an,
They asked the polis band to play The Wearing of the Green,
But the buggers in the Dee-pot didn't know the tyoo-an; so

(Chorus) : They all went up to Monto, Etc.

Queen Vic she came to call on us, she wanted to meet all of us —
'Tis well she didn't fall on us, she's eighteen sto-an !
Then, 'Mister, my Lord Mayor', says she,'Is that all yez have to show to me ?'
'Why, no Ma'am, there's some more,' says he,'Pogue-ma-hone !' Then,

(Chorus) : They took her up to Monto, etc.

SERGEANT WILLIAM BAILEY

Oh! Ser-geant Wil-liam Bai-ley was a man of high re-nown Too-ra-loo-ra-loo-ra-loo-ra - loo. — In search of gal - lant young re-cruits he used to scour the town Too-ra-loo - ra - loo-ra -loo-ra - loo. — His face was full and swarthy,— of medals he had for - ty,— And ribbons on his chest red white and blue It was he what looked the he-ro— and he made the peo-ple stare-o— As he stood on Dun-phy's cor-ner, too-ra - loo.

But alas for human greatness, every dog he has his day, Toor . . .
And Sergeant William Bailey he is getting old and grey, Toor . . .
Some rebel youths with placards, have called his army blackguards,
And told the Irish Youth just what to do.
In spite of fife and drumming no more recruits are coming
For Sergeant Wiliam Bailey tooraloo.

Sergeant William Bailey, what a wretched sight to see, Toor . . .
The back that once was firm and straight is almost bent in three, Toor . . . . . .
No longer youths are willing, to take his dirty shilling
And things for him are looking mighty blue.
He has lost his occupation, let's sing in jubilation
For Sergeant Bailey, tooraloo.

One of the finest satyrical songs to be written by Peadar Kearney. You can almost see Sergeant William Bailey with his forty medals standing at Dunphy's Corner, which by the way was Doyle's Corner, which is now Murphy's Corner. Why do they keep changing the names of Dublin pubs ? Do they not know that half of Dublin's history can be traced from references to pubs, not to mention that all street directions are given from one pub to the other ? Why great names like The Bleeding Horse and The Old Grinding Young were changed to The Falcon and The Poplars respectively I'll never know.

The Recruiting Sergeant has always been one of the most hated characters by the balladmakers in both Ireland and England. In all of the songs about him he always comes out the worst. Peadar Kearney, in this song, humiliates him completely. The following piece is the patter of a recruiting Sergeant Kite who was on the go in 1704, but the substance of his chat remained the same up to the first world war :
'If any gentlemen, soldiers or others have a mind to serve Her Majesty, and pull down the French King; if any prentices have severe masters, any children have undutiful parents; if any servants have too little wages, or any husband too much wife, let them repair to the noble Seargeant Kite, at the sign of the Raven in this good town of Shrewsbury, and they shall receive present relief and entertainment. Gentlemen, I don't beat my drum here to ensnare or inveigle any man; for you must know, gentlemen, that I am a man of honour.

GET ME DOWN MY PETTICOAT

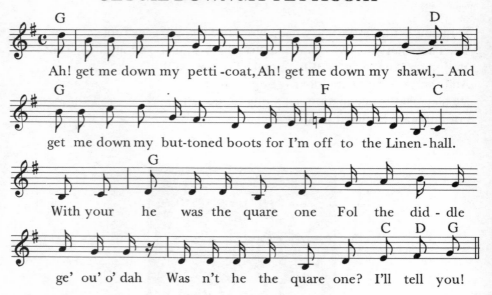

Ah! get me down my petti-coat, Ah! get me down my shawl,— And
get me down my but-toned boots for I'm off to the Linen-hall.
With your he was the quare one Fol the did-dle
ge' ou' o' dah Was n't he the quare one? I'll tell you!

Now if he's joined the army all under a false name
To do me out of my pension it's his oul one's to blame.

Chorus

And if you go to the Curragh Camp just ask for number nine
You'll find three squaddies standing there and the best looking one is mine.

Chorus

And if you go to the fighting line and there to fight the Boer
Will you kindly hould the Dublins back, let the culchies go before.

Chorus

My love's o'er the water, my love he's o'er the sea
My love's o'er the water and left me in the family way.

Chorus

Ah ! get me down my petticoat and get me down my shawl
Get me down my buttoned boots for I'm off to the Linen Hall.

Chorus

 A song dealing with the Dubliners who listed, probably in the fusiliers, in this case to fight the Boers.
There are many songs of the Irish soldier fighting England's wars down through the centuries.
When one hears the rural ballad on this particular subject it usually tells of the big reunion between the
two lovers on the safe return of Johnny from the wars. The Dubliner however has no time for such
sentiment as can be seen in this song. If, as is mentioned in the song, he had a row with the wife, it was
quite common for the soldier to go under a false name so that if he was killed she would get no
pension.

ZOOLOGICAL GARDENS

Ah thun-der and light- ning is no
lark, when Dub- lin ci- ty is in the
dark, If you've a- ny mo -ney come up to the
Park and view the Zoo- lo- gi- cal Gar- dens

I took me mott up to the a-Zoo,
To show her the lions and the kangaroo,
There were he-males and she-males of every hue,
Up in the Zoological Gardens.

Says she to me :'Me lovely son Jack,
I'd love a ride on the elephant's back,'
'If you don't ge'owa that I'll give you such a crack,
All up in the Zoological Gardens.'

We went up there on our honeymoon,
We saw the lion and the hairy baboon,
And we strayed for a while 'neath the silvery moon,
Up in the Zoological Gardens.

I took her up there to see the a-Zoo,
To show her the lion and the kangaroo,
But all she wanted to see was my blue cock-a-too,
All up in the Zoological Gardens.

We left by the gate at Castleknock,
Says she to me :'Sure we'll court on the lock,'
Then I knew she was one of the rare old stock,
From outside the Zoological Gardens.

Oh thunder and lightning is no lark,
When Dublin City is in the dark,
If you've got any money go up to the park,
And view the Zoological Gardens.

This is one of those songs that you will find in almost al traditions, it allows one a chance to be humorously vulgar, giving an opportunity for a good belly laugh without being offensive. Usually there is a double meaning to a situation such as :

'I'd love a . . .'ride' . . .on the elephant's back'

'But all she wanted was to see my blue . . 'Cock-a-too.'

or there will be a play on the names and attributes of the different animals.

In the English tradition there are several songs that tell of a man going the road with his . . 'cock' . . .and the song then goes on to tell you of all the things that happened to his 'cock.' There are others which enlarge on the various organs of the particular animal such as "the Derby Ram' or 'The Herring that came in with the Tide.'

'It took all the men in Derby to roll away his bones,

It took all the women in Derby to roll away his stones.'

This song was a particular favourite of Brendan Behan's, there is a recording of him singing it in true humorous Dublin fashion with emphasis placed on all the appropriate words. There are several different versions to some of the verses I have printed here.

DUBLIN IN MY TEARS

I have tra-velled ma-ny lands, and I still can't un-der
stand, How sad you have be- come on my re- turn
Your poor heart is filled with care, sad and old they left you
there, Your once bright eyes with sor-row soft-ly burn, I can
e- ven sense the change in the sound of child-ren's games, Child-hood
tears and youth's am- bi-tion have all turned to doubt and fear, It's an
age of youth I'm told, yet I've ne- ver felt so old. As
I re- call old Dub -lin in my tears

All the faces that I meet as I roam each one-way street
Reflect the empty statement of the times,
And the old cathedral bell can't be heard above the swell
For the years erased the message in her chimes.
All my childhood friends are gone like the streets where we were born
But the time that it has taken doesn't seem so many years,
They have faded in the gloom with 'Sap' Kelly of the Coombe,
Just the ghost of dear old Dublin in my tears.

There were times when jobs were few, there were hungry days we knew,
Some days so bad their memory I've cursed,
As a prayer I said to God, there on board the 'Princess Maud'
That our children would restore a pride we lost,
But the past they all forsake as they're dancing at your wake
While the heart of Dublin's dying, but nobody really cares,
And the fools as they pass by, laugh to see an old man cry
But I can't forget old Dublin in my tears.

So, gather 'round good friends and true, 'though our numbers they be few
We'll drink one toast before I cross the foam,
Soon in London's dark domain, I'll recall how I became
No more stranger there than here at home.
Now the Liffey flows along as I listen for her song
And the voice of Big Jim Larkin seems to echo in my ears,
But it's just the rafter's ring, to her requiem I'll sing:
Farewell to dear old Dublin in my tears.

Yes, farewell to dear old Dublin in my tears.

Since the first edition of this collection of Dublin songs, the economic situation in the country has
altered greatly. From a position of almost full employment and zero emigration we have come full
circle to a situation of high unemployment and a level of emigration equal to the fifties when
emigration was seen as the only possible solution for the youth of the country.
This is a song written by Brendan Phelan which reflects the atmosphere of the time, however the
young people going abroad today are better educated than ever before and instead of sailing on the
"Princess Maud' they fly Aer Lingus and arrive in London with a confidence in their own ability. They
no longer are faced with spending their life down in a hole (as they did in that other song 'Mc Alpine's
Fusileers') but are just as likely to be the engineer, the architect, the contracts manager or the developer
of the site. It will be interesting to see if this generation will return with the skills which they have
acquired abroad and put them to use in bringing Ireland into the next century, a century where forced
emigration may hopefully be unknown.

THE FOGGY DEW

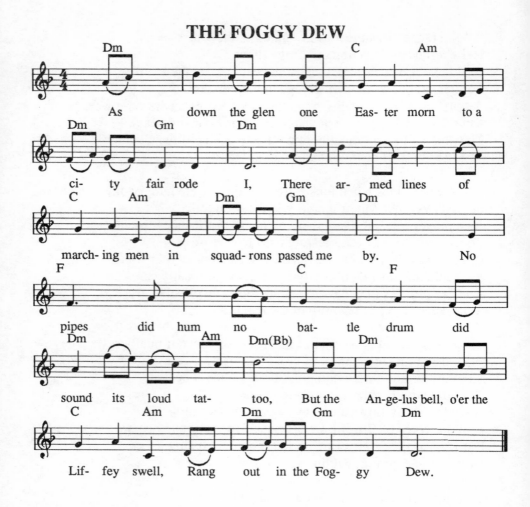

Right proudly high over Dublin town they hung out the flag of war
'Twas better to die 'neath an Irish sky than at Suvla or Sud el Bar;
And from the plains of royal Meath brave men came hurrying through
While Brittania's huns with their long range guns sailed in through the Foggy Dew.

But the night fell black, and the rifles' crack made perfidious Albion reel
'Through that leaden hail seven tongues of flame did shine o'er the lines of steel.
By each shining blade a prayer was said that to Ireland her sons would be true
And when morning broke, still the green flag shook out its folds in the Foggy Dew.

But the bravest fell and the requiem bell rang out mournfully and clear
For those who died that Easter tide in the springing of the year.
While the world did gaze in deep amaze at those fearless men and few
Who bore the fight that freedom's light might shine through the Foggy Dew.

It was England bade our wild geese 'Go! that small nations might be free'
But their lonely graves are by Suvla's waves and the fringe of the great North Sea.
Oh, had they died by Pearses's side or had fought along with brave Cathal Brugha,
Their names we would keep where the Fenians sleep,'neath the shroud of the Foggy Dew.

As back through that Glen I rode again and my heart with grief was sore
For I parted then with these gallant men I never would see no more
But to and fro in my dreams I go and I kneel and I say a prayer for you
For slavery fled, oh you gallant dead, when you fell in the Foggy Dew.

I have said in a note to the song on James Connolly that there were only a good few songs written about the Easter Rising in Dublin in 1916, this is one of those songs. I have liked this song ever since I first heard it sung by my father when I was only a child. At this present time one hears the revisionists of Irish history express doubts as to whether the Easter Rising was really necessary or whether the men who fought and died might not have done so for the highest motives, this song tolerates no ambivalence but gives the full praise due to those men who gave their lives for our freedom.

> 'For slavery fled oh you gallant dead,
> When you fell in the Foggy Dew.'

I never knew where this song came from until my friend Cathal O'Boyle included it in his 'Songs of County Down' and gave the source.

'The words of this song were composed by Canon Charles O'Neill who was parish priest of Kilcoo and later of Newcastle. In 1919 he went to Dublin and attended a sitting of the first Dail Eireann. He was moved by the number of members whose names were answered during the roll call by a cry of 'faoi ghlas ag na Gaill' (locked up by the foreigner) and resolved to write a song in commemoration of the Easter Rebellion. The air to which it is set is an older traditional air also used for the song 'Jackets Green.' The original manuscript of the words and music, in the possession of Kathleen Dallat of Ballycastle, names Carl Hardebeck as the arranger.'

WHEN MARGARET WAS ELEVEN

My fa-ther waved fare- well and the band played tunes of glo- ry, A gi- ant man with rib-bons and be- de-villed dig-ni- ty, A re- gi- men- tal ser-geant, the back- bone of the Em- pire, For God and right- eous glo- ry, bound for High Ger-ma- ny, Sweet Lord I was just se- ven, when Mar-' gret was e- le -ven, They served us war for break-fast and sol-dier's songs for tea. Your fa-ther's gone cam- pain-ing, Was a way of not ex- plain-ing That sol -diers are the li-ving proof of our in -hu -ma- ni- ty. There'll

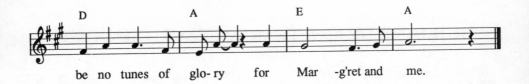

be no tunes of glo-ry for Mar -g'ret and me.

My childhood passed away
Midst tales and lurid stories
Of manufactured glories
And inhuman gallantry
I asked 'When is was over?'
But no one deemed to answer me
And Margaret played the dreaded tune
Called High Germany

My father made it home
But he came without his reason
Two eyes of molten madness
A senseless fool of war
'He's just a child,'my mother cried
'To be dressed in full regalia
And paraded as a hero home
From High Germany

When I was growing up in Chapelizod many of the ciustomers in my father's pub were old soldiers, mostly from the Dublin Fusiliers. They had stories to tell of their time in the fields of Flanders and the action that took place around Ypres which they called 'Wipers'. Mick McGrane would tell how he killed the sniper with his bare hands as he climbed down from the tree where he had been hiding and as a result got a fortnight home on leave. Billy Flaherty could show you the picture of himself as a fine young man in uniform home on leave from the front. So many of the homes you were in as a child had a big brass artillery shell, highly polished, sitting on the window beside the aspidistra.

There was a certain sadness about the soldiers of the 1914-18 war, they never quite got the glory they felt they deserved for their exploits on behalf of the crown. Their glory was overshadowed by the action of the men who stayed at home and fought for the freedom of their own country.

'Ah had they died by Pearse's side,
Or had fought along with brave Cathal Brugha'
Their names we would keep where the Fenians sleep,
'Neath the shroud of the Foggy Dew.'
It was then quite common to see around the streets of Dublin men who had suffered badly in the trenches from the effects of mustard gas or the condition that was usually referred to as 'Shellshock.'

This song written by Pete St.John reflects a time in Dublin's history which hopefully will never come again. It takes away the supposed 'glory' of war as displayed in the movies or on the walls of the officers mess and instead tells of its effect in a small Dublin working class home.

BUILDING UP AND TEARING ENGLAND DOWN

Oh, I've won a he- ro's name with Mc. Al- pine's and Cos-
tain, With Fitz- pa- trick, Mur- phy, Ashe and Wim- pey's gang And I've been
oft -en on the road on my way to draw the dole, When there's
no- thing left to do for John- ny Laing. Now I
used to think that God made the mix- er, pick and hod. So that
Pad- dy might know hell a- bove the ground. I've had
gang- ers big and tough, tell me 'Tear it all out rough!' When you're
build- ing up and tear- ing Eng- land down.

In a tunnel underground, a young Limerickman was found
He was built into the new Victoria line
When the bonus-gang had passed, sticking through the concrete cast
Was the face of little Charlie Joe Devine.
And the ganger-man Mc.Gurk,'Big Paddy' eats the work,
And the gas main burst and he flew off the ground
Oh they swear he said 'Don't slack, I'll not be there until I'm back,
Keep on building up and tearing England down !'

I remember carrier Jack with his hod upon his back
How he one day swore he'd set the world on fire
But his face we've never seen, since his shovel it cut it clean
Through the middle of a big high tension wire.
And I saw old 'Balls' McCall from the big flyover fall
Into a concrete mixer spinning round
Though it was not his intent he got a fine head of cement
When he was building up and tearing England down.

I was on the hydro dam Oh the day that Jack McCann
Got the better of his stammer in a week
He fell from the shuttering jamb and that poor old stutterin' man
He was never ever more inclined to speak.
And no more like Robin Hood will he roam through Cricklewood
Or dance around the pubs in Camden Town
But let no man complain, for no 'Pat' will die in shame
When he's building up and tearing England down.

So come all you navvies bold who do think that English gold
Is just waiting to be taken from each sod
For the likes of you and me could ever get an O.E.B.
Or a knighthood for good service to the hod.
They have a concrete master race for to keep you in your place
And a ganger-man to kick you to the ground
If you ever try to take part of what the bosses make
When you're building up and tearing England down.

(notes on page 90)

DUBLIN IN THE RARE OUL' TIMES

Raised on songs and stories, heroes of renown, Are the
passing tales and glories, that once was Dublin town The
hallowed halls and houses, the haunting children's rhymes That
once was part of Dublin, in the rare old times.

Chorus
Ring-a ring-a Rosie, as the light declines, I remember Dublin city in the rare oul' times.

My name it is Sean Dempsey, as Dublin as can be
Born hard and late in Pimlico, in a house that ceased to be.
By trade I was a cooper, lost out to redundancy,
Like my house that fell to progress, my trade's a memory.

Chorus

And I courted Peggy Dignan, as pretty as you please,
A rogue and child of Mary, from the rebel Liberties.
I lost her to a student chap, with skin as black as coal,
When he took her off to Birmingham, she took away my soul

Chorus

The years have made me bitter, the gargle dims my brain,
'Cause Dublin keeps on changing, and nothing seems the same.
The Pillar and the Met have gone, the Royal long since pulled down,
As the great unyielding concrete, makes a city of my town.

Chorus

Fare thee well sweet Anna Liffey, I can no longer stay,
And watch the new glass cages, that spring up along the Quay.
My mind's too full of memories, too old to hear new chimes,
I'm part of what was Dublin, in the rare ould times.

Chorus

Pete St.John has the knack of writing songs thats seem to go straight to the heart of the Dubliner, it
helps of course that Pete is himself a Dubliner and knows the city and its people intimately.
Even since this little book was first published fifteen years ago, the changes in Dublin have been
immense, new towns have sprung up in the outskirts of the city while the centre of the city has been
allowed to decay. A job that was as secure as Guinness's brewery with a pension at the end of it may
indeed be a thing of the past and the tide of emigration is again flowing at an unacceptable rate taking
with it the best of our youth.
Pete reflects all of these changes in this song 'Dublin in the Rare Oul Times,' it is widely sung and I
think stands a good change of being sung for a long time to come. The song was a favourite of the
great Luke Kelly who sang it widely in his own so inimitable style.

77

THE MAID OF CABRA WEST

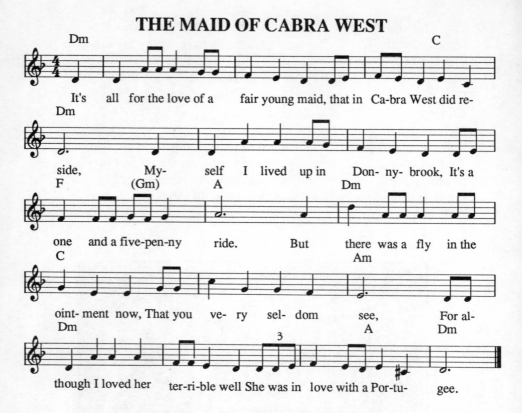

It's all for the love of a fair young maid, that in Ca-bra West did re-side, My-self I lived up in Don- ny- brook, It's a one and a five-pen-ny ride. But there was a fly in the oint- ment now, That you ve- ry sel- dom see, For al-though I loved her ter-ri-ble well She was in love with a Por-tu- gee.

Now he was a nasty piece of goods,
Gonzales was his name,
And he couldn't wait for to get his hands,
On Concepta, who was my dame.
So I made a vow by the Grand Canal,
That I would do him,
For I did not like them Port-u-gees,
And in particular I didn't like him.

So I followed them up to Grafton Street,
One evening just for fun,
Around by the 'Mercers' hospital,
That's next door to the Bartley Dunne's.
I espied them sitting in the corner seat,
They were kissing and holding hands,
And there he was seducing her,
With pints of 'Baby Cham'.

Then I followed him up to his lodgings,
In Rathgar or thereabouts,
And as he walked up the alleyway,
Sure I battered him inside out.
He gave out many an oath and swear,
Till he was dead I'm sure,
Then I lifted up the manhole lid,
And I dropped him down the sewer.

Now when the 'Mott' she heard of this,
She made my life a hell,
And all for the sake of peace and quiet,
Sure I did her in as well.
And now I'm up before the Judge,
To answer for my crime.
He says :'I didn't mind the first one, son,
But not the second time.

So it's all for the love of that fair young maid,
And her Portugese sailor boy,
For the passionate love of that fair young maid,
I've landed in Mountjoy.
And if ever I get out again,
My life I'll change you'll see,
And I'll marry with a 'Mott' from Walkinstown,
Who wouldn't look at a Port-u-gee.

In the rural tradition there are many ballads in praise of the various 'Maids' : 'The Maid of Erin's Isle',
'The Star of Slane', 'The Blazing Star of Drung'. In the fashion of Dublin ballads the sarcastic,
humourous approach is used for 'The Maid of Cabra West'. This is a song that was composed in the
recent past, and since I first heard it sung it has grown by three extra verses. It has much the same
flavour as "Three Lovely Lasses from Kimmage' a favourite of the late, great Luke Kelly.
The Dublin Corporation housing estates each took their turn at being the butt of the comedian's joke;
Kimmage, Crumlin, Cabra, Ballyfermot and Ballymun, so the song can be dated by the reference to
Cabra West or to the pre-metric cost of the bus fare from Donnybrook, one shilling and five pence.

THE BROWN AND YELLOW ALE

As I was go-ing down the road One fine
morn-ing. Oh, the brown and the yel-low ale I
met with a young man with-out a-ny
warn-ing Oh, love of my heart

He asked me if the woman by my side was my daughter,
Oh the brown and the yellow ale,
When I said she was my wife his manner didn't alter.
Oh love of my heart.

He asked me if I'd lend her for an hour and a day,
Oh the brown and the yellow ale,
I said if she thinks it's fair you may take her away,
Oh love of my heart.

She said:'You take the high road and I'll take off with him
Oh the brown and the yellow ale,
And we'll meet again by the ford of the river,
Oh love of my heart.

I was waiting by that ford for an hour and a quarter,
Oh the brown and the yellow ale,
When she came to me t'was without shame I saw her,
Oh love of my heart.

When she told me her story I lay down and I died,
Oh the brown and the yellow ale,
She sent two men for timber and she never even cried,
Oh love of my heart.

A board of alder and a board of holly,
Oh the brown and the yellow ale,
And two great yards of a shroud about me
Oh love of my heart.

Now if my own little mother had never been a woman,
Oh the brown and the yellow ale,
I would sing you many another song about women,
Oh love of my heart.

The first person I heard singing this song in this particular form was the great Dublin singer Dominic Behan. It was a favourite of James Joyce, who himself was a fine singer, coming second only to John McCormack in the Feis Cheoil, an honour of which he hated to be reminded. While Dominic seemed to think that this version was a translation by James Stephens, Richard Ellman in his biography of Joyce suggests that it was Joyce who sang and taught the song to Stephens at their first meeting in Pat Kinsella's pub. Stephens himself later sang the song on a BBC broadcast. There have been several translations of the song from the Irish original "Chuaca Lan De Bui' and many of us learned a simple version of it at singing class in the national school.

It was Sean O'Boyle from Armagh who suggested to me that the significance of the brown and yellow ale was that the old man lost his wife to the young man in question, due to his impotence brought about by drinking too much of the 'Brown and Yellow Ale'.

JAMES CONNOLLY

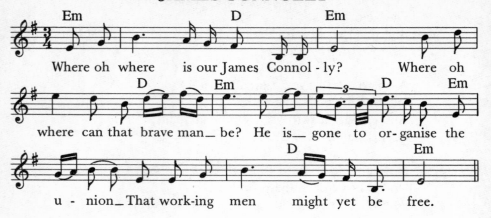

Where oh where is our James Connol-ly? Where oh where can that brave man_ be? He is_ gone to or-ganise the u-nion_ That work-ing men might yet be free.

Where oh where is the citizen army?
Where oh where can the brave band be?
They have gone to join the great rebellion
And break the bonds of slavery.

And who'll be there to lead the van?
Who will be there to lead the van?
Oh who should there be but our James Connolly,
The hero of each working man?

Who carries high our burning flag?
Who carries high our burning flag?
Oh who but James Connolly, all pale and wounded
Carries high our burning flag?

They carried him up to the jail.
They carried him up to the jail.
And 'twas there that they shot him one bright May morning
And quickly laid him in his grave.

Who mourns now for our James Connolly?
Who mourns now for the fighting men?
Oh lay me down in yon green garden
And make my bearers union men.

We laid him down in yon green garden,
With union men on every side
And we swore that we'd make one mighty union
And fill that gallant man with pride.

So come all you noble young Irish men,
Come join with me for liberty.
And we will forge a mighty weapon
And break the bonds of slavery.

 The various rebellions throughout Irish history have each produced a crop of good patriotic songs, and
the 1916 produced very few. This is one of the few. Besides being a leader of the rebellion, James
Connolly was also a leader of the Trades Union movement and the Citizen army mentioned was
originally organised to protect union members at meetings during the formative period when they
came under attack from police and anti-union factions. It then joined in the struggle for national
independence. When the English decided to execute the leaders of the rebellion James Connolly, who
was wounded in the fighting, was unable to stand, so they put him sitting on a chair and shot him.
When I recorded this song some years ago I said in the notes that I knew nothing of its origin. Since
then I have learned that it was written by the Cork-born poet, Patrick Galvin. When I met Patrick
Galvin I mentioned that I had been singing the song for years without knowing that he had written it.
He was pleased that the song had been accepted by the singers and said that it was not important that
they should know who the author was.

KILMAINHAM GAOL, EASTER 1991

For Frank Harte

Roadies in ponytails stringing lights and cables,
A beer can popped in the corner, echo of soundcheck.
Outside, in the filling yard, hum of expectation.
Inside, a quickening pulse.

We pour through the narrow gate under the gallows hook,
In twos and threes, softly becoming an audience.
Before the lights go down we examine each other shyly,
Faces familiar and strange quickening with the night.

The singer surveys his audience, heat rising
To the tricolour and plough overhead.
As the first words of Galvin's lament climb to invoke
James Connolly's ghost, we are joined by the dead.

I say this as calmly as I can. The disembodied dead
Crowded the catwalks, shirtsleeved, disbelieving.
The guards had long since vanished but these
Looked down on us, their faces pale.

I saw men there who had never made their peace,
Men who had failed these long years to accept their fate,
Still stunned by gunfire, wounds, fear for their families;
Paralysed until now by the long volleys of May so long ago.

I think that we all felt it, their doubt and their new fear,
The emblems so familiar, the setting, our upturned faces,
So unreal. Only the dignity of the singer's art
Had power to release them, I felt it, I say this calmly.

I saw them leave, softly, in twos and threes, as the song ended.
I do not know that there is a heaven but I saw their souls
Drift upward like leaves of a dry book, sped out into the night
By volleys of applause, sped out, I hope, into some light at last.

I do not know that I will ever be the same again.
That soft-footed gathering of the dead into their peace
Was like something out of a book. In Kilmainham Gaol
I saw this, I felt this. I say this as calmly and as lovingly as I can

Theo Dorgan

This poem was written by Theo Dorgan after a concert which was held in Kilmainham Gaol to celebrate the seventy-fifth anniversary of the Easter Rebellion. The concert was called the 'Flaming Door,' the title being taken from a poem by W.B.Yeats.

There were actors, poets. musicians and singers there that night, all contributing their talents to celebrate the memory of the men who were executed in that small yard just beside where we were. Some spoke from high up, on the caged-in galleries which run around the central area and which give access to the small prison cells, while others sang and played from the stage on the floor below. I sang Patrick Galvin's lament for James Connolly and as I sang the song the echo came back from high up in the galleries above. I have sung that song hundreds of times, but I have never had a feeling like I felt that night in the centre of Kilmainham gaol.

Some weeks later I received this poem in the post from Theo Dorgan, in it he has managed to convey something of the atmosphere that was abroad that night in Kilmainham gaol.

EASY AND SLOW

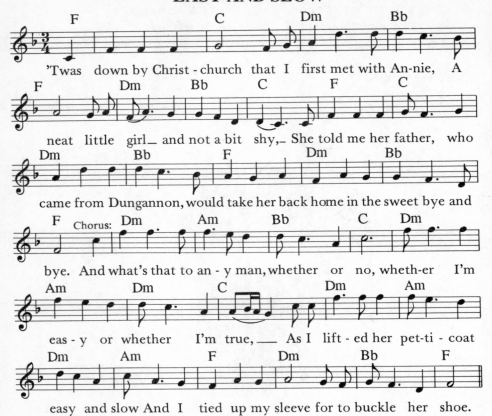

'Twas down by Christ-church that I first met with An-nie, A neat little girl_ and not a bit shy,_ She told me her father, who came from Dungannon, would take her back home in the sweet bye and bye. And what's that to an-y man, whether or no, wheth-er I'm eas-y or whether I'm true, ___ As I lift-ed her pet-ti-coat easy and slow And I tied up my sleeve for to buckle her shoe.

From city or country a girl's a jewel
And well-made for gripping the most of them are.
But any young fellow, he is really a fool,
If he tries at the first time to go a bit far. *Chorus*

We wandered by Thomas Street down to the Liffey.
The sunlight was gone and the evening was dark.
And along by Kingsbridge and begod in a jiffy
Me arm was around her beyond in the Park. *Chorus*

Now if you should go to the town of Dungannon,
You can search till your eyeballs are empty or blind.
Be you sitting or walking or sporting or standing
A girl like Annie you never will find. *Chorus*

I have heard this song sung for years. The first person I ever heard singing it was Dominic Behan, who says he got some of it from Seán O''Casey and the rest from a woman in England. Whenever I ask anybody I hear singing it, the source is inevitably traced back to Dominic.

DUBLIN MADE ME

Dublin made me and no little town
With the country closing in on its streets,
The cattle walking proudly on its pavements,
The jobbers, the gombeenmen and the cheats

Devouring the fair day between them,
A public-house to half a hundred men,
And the teacher, the solicitor and the bank-clerk
In the hotel bar, drinking for ten.

Dublin made me, not the secret poteen still,
The raw and hungry hills of the West,
The lean road flung over profitless bog
Where only a snipe couild nest,

Where the sea takes its tithe of every boat.
Bawneen and currach have no allegiance of mine,
Nor the cute, self-deceiving talkers of the South
Who look to the East for a sign.

The soft and dreary midlands with their tame canals
Wallow between sea and sea, remote from adventure,
And Northward a far and fortified province
Crouches under the lash of arid censure.

I disclaim all fertile meadows, all tilled land,
The evil that grows from it and the good,
But the Dublin of old statutes, this arrogant city,
Stirs proudly and secretly in my blood.

Donagh McDonagh was the son of Thomas McDonagh who was executed as a leader of the 1916 Rising. He had a wide knowledge of the ballads and the poetry in both Irish and English and translated many of the older songs and poems. Donagh had a ballad programme on the radio for years, it was called 'The Ballad Tree,' this was at a time when many were not aware of the existence of the songs, he was one of the first to promote the Clancy Brothers in their early days. Donagh was very much involved with the theatre and I had the pleasure of appearing on the stage of the Abbey with himself and Dan Breen as a prelude to a play about the 'Invincibles.'
I enclose two items by him in this revised edition of Dublin Songs. His fine poem 'Dublin made me' describes not so much what Dublin is but what Dublin is not, it shows the differences as he sees them between Dublin and the other towns of Ireland.

      'I disclaim all fertile meadows, all tilled land'
      'Bawneen and currach have no allegiance of mine'

THE CHARLADIES' BALL

You may talk of your out-ings, your picnics and parties, your
din-ners and dan-ces and hoo-lies and all but wait till I tell yo'f the
gas that we had on the night that we went to the Charladies' Ball. I went
there as Queen Anne and I went with my man, he was dressed as a monkey locked
up in a cage There was pi-rets and pi-rots and Hotten tots and whatnots and
stars that you see on the Music Hall stage. At the Char-la-dies' Ball peo-ple
said, one and all,'You're the belle of the ball, Misses Mul-li- gan' We had
one steps and two steps and the divil knows what new steps We
swore that we ne'er would be dull a-gain, by dad. We had wine, por-ter and

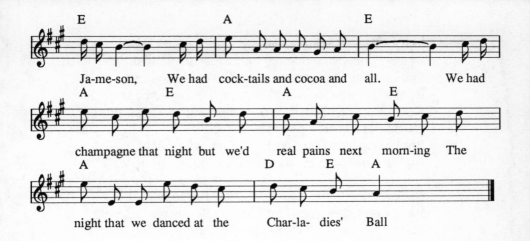

Ja-me-son, We had cock-tails and cocoa and all. We had
champagne that night but we'd real pains next morn-ing The
night that we danced at the Char-la- dies' Ball

Chorus :
At the Charladies' Ball, people said one and all
"You're the belle of the Ball, Mrs. Mulligan."
We had one-steps and two-steps and the divil knows what new steps,
We swore that we never would be dull again, be dad
We had wine, porter and lemonade, we had coctails and cocoa and all.
We had champagnes that night but we had real pains next morning,
The night we danced at the Charladies' Ball.

There was cowboys and Indians that came from Drumcondra,
Sweet Francis Street fairies all diamonds and stars.
There was one of the Rooneys as the clock over Mooney's
And a telegram boy as a message from Mars.
Mary Moore from the Lots was the Queen of the Scots,
With a crown out of Woolworths perched up on her dome.
There was young Jemmy Whitehouse came dressed as a light-house
And a Camden Street Garbo that should have stayed home.

At the Charladies' Ball people said one and all
"You're the belle of the ball, Mrs. Mulligan."
We had one-steps and two-steps and the divil knows what new steps.
We swore that we never would be dull again, be dad,
We had wine, porter and Jameson, we had coctails and cocoa and all.
We had rumbos and tangos, half-sets and fandangos,
The night that we danced at the Charladies' Ball.

Mary Ellen O"Rourke was the Queen of the Dawn.
By one-thirty she loooked like a real dirty night.
Mick Farren, the bester, came dressed as a jester,
He burst his balloon and dropped dead with the fright.
Kevin Barr came as Bovril, "Stops that sinking feeling"
Astride of a bottle, pyjamas and all.
But he bumped into Faust, who was gloriously soused
And the two of them were sunk at the end of the hall.

Chorus —*as before, but with these two last lines:*
We'd a real stand-up fight but we fell down to supper
The night that we danced at the Charladies' Ball.

Again a song made famous by Jimmy O"Dea and written by Harry O'Donovan. The song was written for performing on stage, but it has so much that is Dublin in it, that it has been accepted by the tradition.

Notes on:' Building up and Tearing England Down' (page 74)

I am including this song in a collection of Dublin songs because it was written by Dominic Behan, who did so much to bring Dublin songs out of the shadows and also because it is written about a time which will not come again. Although the events in the song did not take place in Ireland, it is an expression of our people and as such must be considered an intrinsic part of our tradition.

The song tells of the exploits of the Irish navvy on the building sites of England after the war when whole cities as well as a complete new system of roadways were being built.
Although I feel that most of the characters referred to in the song are big strong countrymen, the sarcastic cut which runs thriough the song is definitely of Dublin origin. Dominic of course did not pick up his sarcastic wit off the street, his uncle was Paedar Kearney who was not behind the door in dishing out the sarcasm himself in songs like 'Whack Fol De Diddle' or 'The Row in the Town.'

There are many other songs dealing with that time such as 'McAlpine's Fusileers' and the 'Hot Ashfelt' as well as those that went back to the last century when Paddy came to 'hoke' the potatoes or reap the harvest. With so many Irish navvys now working on the channel tunnel there are bound to be some songs written about Paddy's adventures under the sea probably similar to those who dug the Thames Tunnel in years gone by.

'And what helped Mister Brunel to dig the Thames tunnel,
Sure wasn't it whiskey from old Inishowen.'

Since I started to re-edit this edition of Dublin songs, Dominic Behan has died, he will be sorely missed as a singer and a writer of songs.

Frank Harte may be heard on the following recordings:

Dublin Street Songs/OSS27
Through Dublin City/OSS44
And Listen to My Song/SPINC 994
Daybreak and a Candle End/SPINC 995

All cassettes available from recordshops or from
Ossian Publications, P.O.Box 84, Cork, Ireland

Ossian Publications

Publishers and Distributors of Irish & General Music

Ossian Publications produce a large range of Irish Music
for traditional & classical instruments as well as
collections of tunes, songs, instruction books and items on
the history of Irish Music.

For our complete list of Books, Sheetmusic,
Cassettes, CD's etc, send us an (international)
postal reply coupon and your name and address.

Ossian Publications Ltd.
P.O. Box 84, Cork, Ireland

Printed by Watermans Ltd, Cork

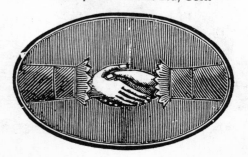